COME BACK
MISS NIGHTINGALE

COME BACK
MISS NIGHTINGALE
TRENDS IN PROFESSIONS TODAY

EDITED BY DIGBY ANDERSON

Published by The Social Affairs Unit

British Library Cataloguing in Publication Data
A catalogue record of this book is available from
the British Library

ISBN 0 907631 79 7

Book production and typesetting by Crowley Esmonde Ltd
Printed and bound in Great Britain by St Edmundsbury Press Ltd

Contents

The Authors

Dr Digby Anderson is founder Director of the Social Affairs Unit and a regular contributor to newspapers and journals.

Dr John P Bunker is Visiting Professor of Health Research and Policy at King's College School of Medicine and Dentistry and University College, London Medical School and Professor Emeritus of Anaesthesia, Stanford University.

Dr Myles Harris is a general practitioner and journalist writing on medical and scientific subjects.

Dr Roger Homan is Principal Lecturer in Religious Studies at the University of Sussex.   He is currently working on a book, *Sacred Art*.

Fernand Keuleneer is a member of the Brussels Bar and a partner of Keuleneer-Storme-Vanneste-Van Varenbergh-Verhelst, a law firm in Brussels. He is also President of the Centre for the New Europe a Brussels-based think tank.

Dr James Le Fanu is a general practicioner, journalist and author of *The Rise and Fall of Modern Medicine* (in press).

Dr Jeffrey Richards is Professor of Cultural History at the University of Lancaster and author of *Films and British national identity*.

Professor Michael M Uhlmann was for many years a partner with a large international law firm. He is now a Senior Fellow at the Ethics and Public Policy Center, Washington DC and Professor of Government in the Washington Semester Program of Claremont McKenna College.

Janet Warren is a practising registered nurse. She has been a ward sister at a London teaching hospital and has worked as a district nurse, a midwife and is now working in general practice.

Professions without virtue?
Introduction and summary
Digby Anderson

The state of the professions
Nursing is in critical decline. So is the profession of the clergy and of
the university academic. Law, as a business is in robust health but law
as a public service is in severe trouble. In apparent contrast, medicine
is in good health. The knowledge basis of medicine, at least its capacity
for effective science-based cure and care, is strong and well publicized.
Doctors are some of the most trusted persons in the community. Yet
even here there are some problems, a substantial threat to professional
independence, bureaucracy, and a high level of disillusion among
doctors. Overall the professions emerge from this study as under threat,
some responding to the threats better than others. What are these threats
and what have been the professional responses?

I do not want ever to enter an English hospital again
A relative of an 88-year-old patient, having seen how that patient was
looked after in hospital confessed, 'I seriously think that death will be
a less painful way out. I certainly do not wish to ever again enter an
English hospital!'. An octogenarian pensioner speaking of the death
of her husband in a hospital ward said, 'Eventually they found him a
bed … but he was so neglected. I asked for an inhaler at least three
times for him, because he couldn't breathe, he never had one until
about two hours before he died – three days later. The day before he
died I was told I could take him home, but I refused because he was so
poorly and thank goodness I was able to be with him for the last 15
hours, the nurses did not come near him unless I asked them to, they
were too busy.'
 Over the last quarter of a century, nurses have been involved in 'a

1

massive retreat from the bedside'. Nursing is now an odd mixture of high-tech efficiency and vastly reduced care. 'The sight of a patient lying in bed surrounded by the very latest in diagnostic equipment but with her food lying congealing on a plate on her bedside locker is commonplace...' Nurse Janet Warren and doctor Myles Harris, surveying the state of nursing after the 'reforms' see it as a profession 'once deeply respected' which has been 'wrecked'. There is an apparent oddity about the parlous state of nursing. Nursing is now more expert than it was. There is now more knowledge and technology to it. Knowledge is often identified as the key characteristic of a profession. How can more knowledge accompany professional decline?

Nursing once characterized by discipline and duty

Nursing has its origins in monasticism from which it derived rules of silence, obedience, ritual and duty. That, together with the huge body of practical and academic knowledge built up by traditional nursing made the old-fashioned ward an efficient, orderly, if austere place in which patients were deeply respected and nurses trusted and also respected. The order and ethos of the old ward depended upon strict discipline and a system of clear rank. Rank has been destroyed by the modern obsessions with 'equality' and informality. Modern management theory has taken the nurse away from the bed to a nurses' station with much patient care delegated to orderlies. The same management thinking has produced the supermarket ward in which staff and patients are turned over at furious pace. Feminism has emphasized the nurse's rights at the expense of her duties.

Nursing in decline both in numbers and quality

More particularly, it was felt that the old apprentice training system would not continue to attract enough nurses because it, allegedly, could not handle new technologies. The technologies were necessary both for the good of the patients and to raise the status of nursing. The ideal was a degree in nursing, a 'career' in nursing, the new nurse not a practised bedside carer but a 'manager'. The new training was also anti-elitist and more 'supportive'. In short, the ideologies of the nineteen sixties from feminism to managerialism were let loose on nursing. The result? Far from boosting recruitment, numbers entering nursing education fell by some 39 per cent. Nursing numbers are heading for 'a catastrophe'. The quality of nursing already is one.

The neglected importance of character in professionalism
In retrospect it is obvious that nursing was a profession especially
dependent on a tradition and one which emphasized the importance
of character. The traditional nurse was not a bundle of expert tricks
but a person of certain virtues, committed to a certain life which was
shared with her nursing colleagues. Brash managerialism, rights-
obsessed feminism, and modern informality either don't understand
or positively hate to acknowledge the role of character, vocation,
authority and tradition. So that they may have their way, the sick are
now suffering. Nursing is a stark example of what happens to a
profession when virtue is scorned.

**The old university, a place for acquiring the character of a
scholar**
Academe provides another example. University academics may appear
to do what they always did, writing books, undertaking research,
attending conferences, teaching students, refereeing and reviewing,
supervising. But if one looks deeper, argues Professor Jeffrey Richards,
the values which motivated these activities have disappeared or have
at any rate been radically transformed. There has been 'a treason of
the intelligentsia'. The old university was not about learning expertise
for its own sake but the acquisition of habits of mind and service. It
was about acquiring a certain scholarly character. That character valued
knowledge but it valued wisdom more. Universities transmitted not
technique but civilization, that is, certain values and a capacity for
judgement. One particular value was a commitment to truth, fairness
and humanity, another was that of collegiality. The academic was not
an isolated scholar but a member of a community where each helped
and respected the other. It was also an exclusive elite and proud to be
so.

The importance of collegiality no longer recognized
This ideal endured for a remarkably long time, up until the mid-
nineteen sixties. The boundaries so necessary to this sort of university
– exclusivism, collegiality, shared tradition and outlook – were destroyed
by what Christopher Lasch called 'the revolt of the elites' following
the cultural revolution of the nineteen sixties. The new values were, as
in nursing, egalitarianism and informality, a repudiation of character
and character training, abolition of collegial institutions such as
common rooms, and the eradication of distinctions between high and

mass culture. The scholarly gentlemen respecting each other became warring tribes outbidding each other in their rejection of Western civilization and the past.

The academic caught between egalitarianism and managerialism

What the relativist revolution did not destroy was finished off by the new managerialism. Communities of scholars became businesses with increasing emphasis on 'outputs' and, as with nursing, 'throughput rates'. What was taught was now vocational and marketable skills. What was previously wisdom was now another product. In particular, the demand for accountability generated an enormous bureaucracy which has become an end in itself.

There was, and is, a world of difference between the high-knowledge profession of the academy and the traditionally practitioner-based nursing but both these dissimilar professions have fallen to several of the same forces: from the left, egalitarianism, informality and relativism, from the right, managerialism. Interestingly, the solution is similar for both, a return to the old values and institutions.

The clerisy have fallen even further than the nurse or the don

The professional state of the clergy is, if anything, worse since they had the furthest to fall. Not only were the clergy of the middle ages a profession, they were almost *the* profession, with priests as doctors, architects, lawyers, academics, scientists as well as preachers and administrators of the sacraments. Their monasteries were also the powerhouses not only of Christianity but of Western civilization itself. As *the* profession they had privileges and immunities in addition to the privileges which a profession usually has. Dr Roger Homan charts the loss of these privileges. It is a long list. Immunity from civil law was lost long ago. Since then there have been other losses: a loss of control over education and poor relief, a loss of clientele through membership attrition, the rise of the laity and the taking on of clerical tasks by the laity, culminating in the recent institution of unpaid clergy. Income has plummeted. But clergy have also lost things of a different sort. The decline in sacred aspects of the church – the cult of informality again – has led to the status of the clergyman being regarded as less special. He has lost status, authority, a professional language, even a clear body of knowledge as his own. Here too, training has played its part in the decline of the profession with the new emphasis on skills and management replacing that on character. Increasingly, the clergyman is what he does, not what he is, and what he does many non-clergymen are now doing too.

Clerical authorities colluded in the decline

The decline of the clergy started long before that of nursing or academe. In many respects it merely reflects a general secularization of society. But there are similarities as well. Homan describes how church authorities have colluded in de-professionalisation by their acceptance of the informality ethos, their erosion of the sacred through liturgical reform, through changes in ordination training and blurring the differences between the lay and the ordained. At first sight, professional decline may appear to be the result of hostile external forces but on closer examination the profession turns out to have invited them to occupy its heartland.

The lawyer once had twin obligations – to his client and to 'law' itself

The nurse is, or was, dedicated to her patient. Although the academic scholar and the priest are dedicated to their student or parishioner, they have an even stronger dedication, not to a person but to an idea and an ideal, to truth. With the lawyer the twin obligations are more evenly matched and to some extent in conflict. He has an obligation to his client. He also has one to 'law'. In an age when the lawyer is the butt of jokes, it should be remembered that the rule of law is a chief characteristic of democratic and decent societies. Law is a foundation stone of the good society and lawyering is a public calling as well as a private service. Or, at any rate, it was. Lawyers, as Fernand Keuleneer reminds us, were supposed to defend the client's interest while upholding the letter and spirit of the law. 'The lawyer who looks upon the law exclusively as an instrument to enhance his client's interests, without consideration for the civilized public order [is more] a predator than a lawyer'. He uses 'the law as a weapon' and the meeting of lawyers is a form of 'civil warfare', a far cry from the order traditionally associated with the rule of law.

Both Michael Uhlmann, writing about law in the USA, and Fernand Keuleneer from Brussels, point to the decline of the public calling element in law. Partly, believes Keuleneer, it is because law is now fragmented. It is specialised with different types of lawyer knowing little about others' specialities. If there is no longer any one thing, 'law', how can there be loyalty to it? According to Uhlmann, this fragmentation results in a loss of collegiality, lawyering as a communal life shared by other lawyers, and this loss of collegiality increases the fragmentation. The same sort of process as has been seen in academe. Also, as in academe, expertise is replacing wisdom. This is partly because of the case nature of law, partly because, although law always was both a trade and a profession, the trade element, simple greed some would say, is now dominant. Furthermore, unlike the academic, the lawyer is not doing the same things he always did, albeit led by different values, he is actually doing different work in a different institution.

The quantity of government regulation has altered the work done by lawyers

The lawyer works in a law firm and, increasingly, in a large law firm. Over a quarter of lawyers, reports Uhlmann, work for governments, corporations or universities. And the character of the work they do is new. Work for corporations comprises making money and deflecting government regulation. Many lawyers have little contact with courts; they are advisers to corporations or government departments. Certainly, few are like the old family lawyers who built up relationships with clients over generations. Nowadays you merely go to the lawyer specializing in X. The growth of regulation, especially group rights regulation and environmental regulation, has changed the character of law. And so has the rise of the 'billable hour'.

As with the clergy and nursing, another powerful agent of change has been how members of the profession are trained. The old apprenticeship or *staggiare* system is in decline. Even more important according to Uhlmann have been the new elements of legal education, 'Critical Legal Studies and the Law and Economics movements, which reduce legal knowledge to a subset of a more architectonic understanding – in the first case to the interests of gender, race and class ... in the latter, to the motivations of *homo economicus*.' Both belittle character and reduce wisdom to mere technique. Status and monetary reward replace public calling or, in the case of rights law, a calling to serve the whole public.

Old wisdoms replaced by new techniques

Whatever the complex inter-relationships of these factors, there is no doubt about one of the major casualties. It is the character-based notion of a profession. The emphasis on expertise will favour the technically-proficient candidate seeking entry to law school or firm over the honest and publicly dedicated. The training will ignore or corrupt character and so will the types of work and new values.

What we are beginning to see with the law, is why professional decline is more than a professional matter. If a society has worse lawyers, it does not just mean that litigants or defendants get a worse or more expensive deal, it means that a foundation block, some would argue *the* foundation block, of a decent and orderly society is damaged.

Medicine apparently in better shape: an improving knowledge base

Medicine, the profession of the physician, is in much better shape than law, nursing, the clerisy or academe. Unlike the case of the clergy, doctors' knowledge has actually increased and their monopolistic control of it has been maintained: as yet there is no equivalent to the intrusion of the laity. Curative medicine at one point did, however, face a similar danger. As Professor John Bunker points out, it was challenged by the rise of public health. The challenge was the claim that it was public health provisions which, for instance, 'were responsible for the sharp decline in infectious disease experienced early in the twentieth century, most of which had been achieved before the introduction of many of the vaccines, and well before the availability of antibiotics'. Stung by such criticism, medicine made a considerable effort both to assess its own effectiveness rates and to give an account of them. It is now clear that 'since [1945] there has been an explosion of new and effective medical treatments, many of which lead to substantial improvements of health [and] an equivalent, on average, to the halving of the death rate at every age throughout life.' Medicine took steps to measure its outcomes, to initiate medical audits, to introduce medical liability and, while accepting some reduction in the autonomy of individual doctors, maintained the autonomy of the profession overall. The justification for autonomy is expertise and self-control. Medicine possessed both.

Even so, doctors are demoralized

Dr James Le Fanu agrees about the expertise. Indeed, he rates it even more highly. 'The achievements of medicine in the 50 years since the War rank as one of the most sustained epochs of human endeavour since the Renaissance.' He agrees with Bunker that we now have evidence-based medicine. Yet he finds doctors, in Britain, to be demoralized. Fifty per cent say they would choose another profession if they had their time again. The fault is not with the expertise. It is with other aspects of professionalism. Doctoring is about the application of facts to cases. It involves the use of judgement and a sort of paternal beneficence towards the patient; a sense of justice and honesty Dr Le Fanu refers to as 'integrity'. But to make this collection of attributes work, another is needed: independence.

The threat to independence
In Britain, that independence has been attacked. A new management system means doctors are not in charge. In hospitals especially, they are increasingly employees controlled by a new managerial class. (The loss of control with US Health Maintenance Organizations is somewhat similar.) The old collegial, hierarchical hospital ethos has been destroyed as much in relation to doctors as to nurses. Old ties of loyalty to institutions have been broken. The culprit here is outside medicine. It is misguided government policy. But medicine has also been guilty of professional lapses, in the USA by over-treatment, in the UK by failing to live up to its NHS obligations while making money in private practice. The abuses may be those of a minority, but the profession has not been seen to be disciplining them.

The very success of medicine has created a need to control costs and the perceived lack of professional discipline has allowed the state to bring in a new class of cost-containing managers. The most noticeable result of this has been a burgeoning bureaucracy. Even more important though is the loss of professional integrity and independence.

Professional decline caused by inattention to the 'character' aspects of professionalism
A central cause, then, of professional decline is the failure to take the 'character' aspects of professionalism seriously. There is a tendency to view professions as built on knowledge and to think of the ethical and characterological aspects as appendages to boost respectability or as a reassurance that monopolistic knowledge will not be abused. The purpose of this collection of studies is to prove that professions are, or should be, more than expertise. They require a commitment both to those served and to an idea and an ideal. They require collegiality. Their knowledge is not mere facts and technique but wisdom and

judgement. In short, as Homan expresses it, what makes a profession a profession is the sort of person who practises it. The implication is that professional 'training' should be regarded not as knowledge inculcation but as the formation of a certain sort of person. Only those of good character should be accepted and only those of good character accredited and licensed.

If the professions and their training institutions will not adopt such politically incorrect reforms, then professions will continue to decline. That will matter for the sick, for the student, for the defendant, for the parishioner. But it will also matter for society in general because professions have another role which is to act as exemplars of good behaviour to those in other jobs. All jobs have a professional aspect to them, and a society with decaying professions will itself surely decay.

1

Extinguishing the lamp

the crisis in nursing

Janet Warren and Myles Harris

The monastic basis of medicine:
silence, obedience, courtesy and authority

Nursing remained a traditional profession until 1970. Like medicine it was modelled on monasticism from which it was derived. Nurses obeyed rules of silence, obedience, ritual, courtesy and duty. Nurses wore habits or uniforms. They aspired to ideals of heroic self-sacrifice and service. A nurse who died in the 1950s of an infectious illness caught from a patient would be privately honoured, but never mourned publicly. Tens of thousands gave up marriage and family to follow nursing.

It is difficult to recreate the atmosphere of a traditional ward of the late nineteen fifties. It centred on the figure of the ward sister, in blue uniform with a distinctive cap, frilly sleeves which she took off before starting work, and a cloak. Ward sisters were often unmarried, and devoted to their work. They carried an air of absolute authority. The ward sister was the pivot around which the hospital turned.

The sense of structure, formality and discipline of the ward she directed was intense. Her nurses wore traditional uniforms; they were forbidden to have hair longer than shoulder length. Personal jewellery was banned, dresses were to be no more than 12 inches off the floor. Nurses were not expected to marry while they were in training and were only allowed to live out of the nurses' home in their third year and then only with the permission of the Matron.

The formal routine created an atmosphere of calm and purpose. As a result there were queues of applicants to enter nursing. Nurses took an intense pride in their profession, felt secure and needed, and were rewarded with the appreciation of their patients.

This world which may seem hostile and alien to some modern readers needs to be put in perspective. Barely 150 years before, hospital patients were largely left to their own devices. If they could not feed themselves, wash or visit the toilet, or had no relatives to help them, they usually died. Most of us are familiar with Dickens's character Sarah Gamp, the drunken midwife *cum* corpse washer, swigging brandy by the fire while her patient died in labour upstairs. Not only did Florence Nightingale throw Sarah Gamp and her brandy bottle into the street, she replaced her with sober, educated young women with a sense of vocation, discipline and profession. She taught that the purpose of nursing is to do those things for the sick they cannot do themselves; that the nurse's duty is to be at the bedside – always. By the 1950s and early 1960s, Nightingale nursing had reached its zenith. Wards were safe, clean and everywhere there was a nurse at hand.

Washing, feeding and dressing patients

Patients were washed, fed, given medicines, helped to get in and out of bed if they could not do so by themselves, prepared for operations, had their wounds dressed and their relatives kept informed of their progress. Particular attention was given to washing and feeding those who could not do it for themselves. Nurses took breakfast, lunch and supper to bedridden patients. So important was this thought 20 years ago that each lunchtime the sister personally supervised the serving of the food from a trolley placed in the centre of the ward. Nurses bathed bedridden patients, made their beds and changed their sheets.

An important feature of this was the 'back round'. People lying immobilized in bed for long periods by pain or sickness can develop ulcers on the points where their weight touches the bed. These can become as large as small dinner plates and can kill. Back rounds involved teams of nurses turning the patients and rubbing their backs every two hours. The number of bedsores in a ward are an accurate gauge of the ability, training and dedication of a hospital's nurses and the efficiency of its administrators. Their successful treatment depends on meticulous and constant attention to detail. Bedsores are now common. In the traditional ward they were rarely heard of.

While feeding and washing the patients was going on, other nurses were administering injections, changing dressings, giving out medicines, checking fluid balance charts, taking blood pressures, and emptying bedpans. Every day either the sister or a staff nurse went around the ward with a member of the medical staff. Once or twice a week a grand round conducted by the consultant took place which all members of the medical and nursing staff were expected to attend. (Today, feminist theory dictates that a nurse will only visit a patient with a doctor if she feels her presence is necessary.)

A huge body of practical and academic knowledge was built into traditional nursing. As a result, the Nightingale ward was the scene of some of the great therapeutic advances of the century. The first successful heart and kidney transplants, open heart surgery, treatment with the new anti-cancer drugs possibly all took place on Nightingale wards. This is in contrast with today where, despite high-tech equipment and modern drugs, poor nursing results in patients returning again and again to hospital to have complications of neglect, such as bedsores or self-injury treated. 'When he [an 82-year-old man] went home he had an ulcer on his leg from an injury he got when he struck his leg against the side of the bed. He also had diarrhoea from the drugs he was given. Both went unnoticed by the nursing staff. Untreated, the ulcer grew to the size of a small saucer. It took his GP over six months to get him on his feet again.'

Security and respect
The formal, disciplined world of the Nightingale ward evoked a feeling of security and respect among patients. Even if you died you knew the nurses would carry out the last offices, washing your corpse and preparing it for the grave. (Today bodies are quickly bagged, dumped into a metal container and rolled away to be hosed with disinfectant in a distant mortuary.) As with any formal system, a genuine feeling of warmth flourished beneath its surface. Nurses were trusted and respected. Nobody thought of individual nurses as paragons of self-discipline – they were after all young women – but the profession and its traditions were trusted. The British had faith in their nurses.

The modern ward is a very different place. The first thing a visitor will notice is that the silence, tranquillity and routine of the Nightingale ward has vanished. Modern wards, especially in large teaching hospitals in our cities, are immensely noisy places. There is an endless procession of visitors, televisions blare, radios play. Ancillary staff, management, social workers and technicians move constantly in and out of the ward. Telephones ring and sleep is almost impossible.

Today, noise, lack of rank, confusion
With this sense of rushed informality has come a complete dismantling

of the old ward ethos. The ward sister, distinctive in her special uniform, has vanished to be replaced by a ward manager often in civilian clothes. Modern nursing eschews rank. The uniforms of all nurses, if they are worn, tend to be the same. The lack of a distinctive uniform, or even its absence, emphasizes that the ward sister is not there to give orders to her nurses but merely to administer. Management theory insists that each nurse on the ward (there are no longer any student nurses) is a professional in her own right. There is no giving and taking of orders; these are thought of as elitist or even sexist. As a result nurses now work in small autonomous teams, each pair responsible for the care of two or three patients. The sister's job is not to give orders but to advise. She arranges treatment protocols, ensures that the ward is kept staffed and properly supplied, organizes staff rosters and attends planning meetings. Most of her work is carried out from behind a computer console or in a distant office. Care is fragmented.

The absence of distinctive uniforms makes it very difficult for patients to link any of the parts of the ward structure together. 'Who on earth is that?' is the thought which goes through many a patient's mind. It also goes through the minds of many of the staff. One of the writers – once a patient himself – remembers being approached by an elderly lady in street clothes in a well-known teaching hospital who introduced herself as Mary and to his astonishment took out a large syringe and asked to take his blood.

The retreat from the bedside
Visitors to post-Nightingale wards are often struck by the fact that nurses are more likely to be found at the nurses' station than at the bedside. In the past ten years nursing 'reforms' have resulted in a massive retreat from the bedside. Hours can be spent consulting ward protocols and filling in forms at the ward station. A great deal of routine care is now carried out by non-nursing staff. The nurses no long serve the patients their food. This is done by ward orderlies, again according to written protocols drawn up by a central bureaucracy. Food is often placed by the bed of a sick patient and if not eaten is gathered up and the contents noted and entered in a log. It can be some days before anyone realizes that the patient is off his food. A recent review of patients in British hospitals found many of them to be malnourished, some dangerously so. The sight of a patient lying in bed surrounded by the very latest in diagnostic equipment but with her food lying congealing on a plate on her bedside locker is commonplace. Catering,

ward cleaning, supplies and ancillary services are all centrally directed.

Up to three patients per bed

Patients and staff are turned over at a furious pace. 'Hot bedding', making sure a bed is used almost non-stop by up to three different patients a day, is common. Care can be fragmentary as staff are moved from ward to ward in an attempt to 'maximise throughput'. Patients may be washed in some hospitals, in others they are badly neglected. Attention to the small details of patient comfort, so essential to survival, no longer take precedence over technology or throughput. It is often possible to see a patient on the latest form of respirator with uncombed, matted hair. An old-age pensioner of 80 recalls, 'I had two major operations in four days, then they decided I needed a bath. I was lowered into the bath sitting on a chair, then I was forgotten, I was too weak to pull a cord, I was covered in bedsores …'

Bogus friendship

Weirdly contrasting with this sense of social isolation, with the feeling of being ill in a supermarket, with patients being left unfed or gazing confusedly at strangers in civilian clothes who arrive to carry out intimate routines on their bodies, is the enforcement of the rule that patients are to be addressed by their Christian names. This managed informality, a bogus hand of friendship outstretched in such an alien and hostile place, devastates many elderly patients who feel they have entered a world with no social rules. Complaint, they soon learn, is fairly useless. Many nurses now employ assertiveness techniques, an extremely effective form of verbal control where a bullying eye contact is maintained with the patient while repeating a simple message over and over again.

Anybody who has been subject to this type of approach when he has been ill is unlikely to forget it. Modern wards are nasty, alien places. Patients hate them and are beginning to take some of that hatred out on what was once a deeply respected profession, nursing. A relative of an 88-year-old patient, having seen how the latter was looked after in hospital, confessed: 'I seriously think death will be a less painful way out. I certainly do not wish to ever again enter an English hospital!'

Growing patient hostility to nurses

Yet nursing leaders, secure in their endless rounds of management seminars, position papers and new protocols for continuing nurse education, are completely unaware of the chasm that has opened between the patient and his nurse. One, a leading nurse educator, told me: 'There is a move [by the nursing profession] from being aloof and fairly authoritarian, of not putting professions on a pedestal, not actually promoting mystique around some professional practice but deconstructing it in a way which is far more engaging of the people we deal with ...'

The reality? An octogenarian pensioner witnessing the death of her husband. 'Eventually they found him a bed ... but he was so neglected. I asked for an inhaler at least three times for him, because he couldn't breathe, he never had one until about two hours before he died – three days later. The day before he died I was told I could take him home, but I refused because he was so poorly and thank goodness I was able to be with him for the last 15 hours, the nurses did not come near him unless I asked them to, they said they were too busy.'

The fall of nursing to feminism and careerism
How has this happened? In the late 1960s nursing changed. It became stridently combative, 'rights based' and feminist. Nursing began to be billed as part of a wider struggle for better consumer rights, equality for minorities, 'gays', any group which could be used as a means of exerting leverage for more pay and a 'better' image. Nursing leaders realized that in an expanding consumer economy focused on youth and the contraceptive pill, traditional nursing would seem out of date and irrelevant. Having to dress up as a Victorian serving-maid, cloister yourself in a nurses' home for three years and take orders from ruthless old maids in the form of the traditional ward sister was unlikely to attract recruits of the Beatle generation.

'Image' was of vital importance. Young women would only be attracted to nursing if it coincided with the new world of consumer expectations and female independence. The hospital, said the new thinking, would, within 20 years, become a health supermarket, the patient a consumer. A patient's rights, his expectations and needs, would become the watchword of good nursing. It is why, 30 years later, nurses talk like employees of Hewlett Packard or Ford. Nursing is now a corporate service industry selling a product called 'health care'.

For this to happen, the old images of authority – the matron with her cap, the cloistered nurses' home, the idea of obedience to a male-dominated medical hierarchy – had to be swept away. The existing nursing structure was dismantled in favour of a management system called 'Salmon'. Salmon was Lord Salmon, chairman of the J Lyons grocery and tea empire and famous for Lyons Corner House in London. Lord Salmon was contracted by a Conservative government in 1963 to review the existing management structure of the NHS and to introduce modern management techniques into it. The report by his committee in 1966, titled 'Senior Nursing Staff Structures in the NHS', laid an axe to the roots of nursing tradition similar to that taken to the railways by his colleague, Dr Beeching. In both cases the idea of service was replaced by efficiency. Beeching tore up thousands of miles of railway track, Salmon tore up the old ward structure. In both cases we are still living with the consequences.

Replacing service with efficiency
'Salmon' did away with the old nursing ranks. His report, which took nearly a decade for its results to flower, took a generation of highly experienced ward sisters, who until then had maintained the Nightingale ward traditions, and moved them into offices far from their patients. The aim, ostensibly, was to create a career structure which could take the nurse in a series of steps away from the bedside to the very highest levels of health management. Nursing care was to be directed from managerial offices far from the ward. In reality, Salmon was to create a new ward structure and a new type of nurse who would be the servant of the NHS bureaucracy, not its master.

The carrot to draw the older sisters from the ward was pay. It was made almost impossible for them to retire with a decent pension unless they accepted the new posts. The real agenda however was a determination by reformers to upgrade nursing's 'image.' Washing the sick would not teach you much about accounting or forward health planning. The three obligations of the nurse based on the corporal works of mercy, – to comfort, feed and bathe the sick, the most important part of nursing, and essential to patients survival – suddenly came to be seen as embarrassing reminders of the days when nurses were merely dumb helpmeets of a male medical profession The new nurse would not take orders from doctors. She would decide herself what was best. None of this would be possible without a complete revamp of the traditional nurses' training. Florence Nightingale may have dealt in bedpans and brooms, the modern nurse would have to understand blood gases and renal dialysis. In the 1940s and 1950s she may have had to oversee the feeding of 40 sick patients; 30 years on, in the 1980s and 1990s, she would have to manage complex budgets and work a computer. A university education would be essential for the new nurse. A university education was vital to status. Without status, nursing recruitment would fall.

Using training to up the status of nursing: nurses as managers

Nursing training would, therefore, have to change. Until around 1988, training was in the form of a ward apprenticeship. After three months of preliminary training student nurses were put to work on the wards. The principle was to give the young nurse maximum exposure to the sick. Although theory was not neglected – the old apprentice nurses had to spend long hours in study – it held second place to what was learnt at the bedside. It was, for instance, possible for a young woman barely six months out of school to find herself working at night in a ward full of sick and dying patients.

But the aim now was to train a new nurse for a new century. Nurses would still care for their patients but a lot more of the routine bedside care would be delivered by semi-skilled workers trained in simple tasks. There would be washers, floor cleaners, bedpan emptiers, food labellers, property clerks, corpse carriers and porters. For a few years nurse managers would direct them, but in the long run these workers would have their own independent hierarchy run by outside contractors. This would leave nurses to get on with more 'professional' tasks such as undertaking the work previously done by junior medical staff, pure research, taking part in hospital management, and sitting postgraduate degrees. By 1995, all traditional nursing schools had closed.

The old training schemes were replaced by Project 2000, a much heralded university course in 'Nursing Studies'. Students on Project 2000 could take a course leading to a diploma. Degrees in nursing would also be available. Project 2000 was born out of another political mirage, 'Health for All by the Year 2000', a plan by the United Nations to offer the entire world's population equal access to health care. 'Health for All' hoped to deliver free contraception, education, and free abortions to women all over the world by the millennium. Project 2000 was the up-market version of 'Health for All'. Instead of health, which she already had, western woman would be offered degrees in nursing, the chance to translate her natural instincts for compassion and detail into a tradeable educational qualification. A woman's role over the centuries, offering care and compassion for the afflicted, would be formalized into a degree.

The new course would be rich in feminist messages. While traditional subjects such as anatomy, physiology and pharmacology were still taught, the new deconstructionist interpretation of medicine, the 'shopper's charter' view of the patient and those who helped him, became the centre point of the course. The year 2000 would see patients rebranded as 'clients' in search of a premium after sales service. Paternalism was out, consumerism in. The new nurse would supply 'care packages' like goods off of the shelf in a supermarket. 'I was very well serviced' said one patient 'but not nursed'. The need to 'rebrand' the nurse in her own mind was paramount. Accordingly student nurses were taught not how to feed the sick but offered time to reflect on their own status, *vis a vis* the male-dominated, oppressive hierarchy of the NHS. The NHS was presented as a paradigm of sickness, a sickness-causing engine in its own right. There was fear that if student nurses spent too much time in NHS hospitals they would be contaminated with 'a sickness model of health care'.

In the early days of Project 2000 such ideas were enthusiastically prosecuted. Nurses were only granted limited access to wards – and then only as 'observers' – until they had completed their training. Not only would they be in danger of imbibing the sickness model of looking after the ill, it was feared that if they did they might be exploited by a male medical hierarchy lurking in the background waiting to set young women to washing the sick. Lest she should be taken advantage of, she was rigorously policed by tutors to make sure she did not work. The old idea of a student nurse being put in charge of a ward at night became in nursing circles the equivalent of a charge of child abuse. Myths were taught to new student nurses about the old Nightingale wards. They were portrayed as Dickensian workhouses in which nurses were deprived of any emotional support by a hard and unforgiving discipline.

The result: declining entrants for nursing careers

To correct past 'abuses' therefore, the new teaching was 'supportive'. Nurses were carefully checked for their reactions to even visiting a ward as observers. Educational theorists emphasized the need for learning to take place in a 'nurturing and supportive' environment. The students were encouraged to develop an informal style when dealing with patients, addressing them by their Christian names and eschewing uniforms. A great deal of 'research' was done on these courses, often of very poor quality. What exactly is learnt on Project 2000 courses is difficult to assess. They are held in contempt by many student nurses, and trained nurses frequently complain of the lack of practical experience on the part of new graduates. There are also signs of growing levels of illiteracy among new graduates. Job applications contain frequent howlers. Lecture notes prepared by staff seem little better. Barbarisms such as 'Use "man" to mean both female and male is inaccurate' are distressingly common.

This would be highly amusing if it were not for the case that, as in other life and death professions such as flying, medicine or the army, an inability to write simple, correct English is dangerous. Numeracy is also a problem. There have been complaints that nurses cannot calculate drug doses because they lack simple mathematical skills.

Literacy and numeracy are not all that are at stake. Project 2000 has led to a major crisis in recruitment. From 1987 until 1994 the number of young women entering training had fallen by 39 per cent, a fall blamed almost entirely on pay and poor conditions. However the biggest single fall (of 19 per cent) was between 1992/93 and 1993/94. Numbers fell from 20,694 to 16,737 just as Project 2000 became universal.

Pay not to blame for drop in recruitment

But does pay have such an effect? In 1988/89, under Mrs Thatcher's government, nurses pay rose from 72 per cent of average non manual earnings to 84 per cent. This had no effect on recruitment of student nurses or little effect on the number of qualified nurses in employment. These numbers, a combination of the longer working lives of women nurses and the use of contract labour, continued a slow rise until 1992 and then began to decline.

Among student nurses a slow decline in recruitment had been going on for a decade, some of it was due to the closure of a two year course for state enrolled nurses, women of modest educational abilities who had made a major contribution to nursing in the past. Nursing theorists felt that such short courses did nothing to improve nursing's 'academic' image and they were wound down. However by 1991 most of these candidates had either transferred to a three year course or had left nursing. In 1993/94 recruitment began to fall dramatically. This was the time when new administrative arrangements for recruiting nurses for Project 2000 were becoming general. It fell sharply again the following year.

Prior to the introduction of university diplomas for nurses, student nurses were hired by individual hospitals, trained there and usually went on working in them for at least a couple of years after qualification. Nurses it was said, possessed 'brand loyalty'. They tended to stay on at the hospital they trained in for at least a year or two after qualification. While they were students they worked along side qualified nurses as part of the staff. They took part in the work of the hospital, they were to be seen every day on the wards. They saw the hospital that trained them as 'theirs.'

Such simple loyalty enraged nursing reformers, who accused the old ward apprenticeship system of exploiting young women as 'a pair of hands', extracting as much work out of them as they could for a minimum of training. Training was an education, not a source of cheap labour. Future nurses would be loyal to their universities not their hospitals.

From now on nurses were to be trained in a distant campus, only visiting the hospitals as students. A complex process of 'commissioning' university places was started. Places were purchased each year at universities by hospital trusts in conjunction with central government. Officials have proved extremely reluctant to explain the practical details of commissioning. But it is not hard to imagine the complex negotiations, position papers and interdepartmental point scoring that would have replaced what was once a straightforward exercise even if it did not involve central authority, the hire of a young woman to train as a nurse in her local hospital. The traditional interview of a local girl by a shrewd and knowledgeable matron usurped by the tedious foolishness of educational jargon mongers, placemen and health and safety sinecurists, stirred vigorously with a long spoon held by the Treasury. In addition, commissioning meant that the Treasury's view that fewer nurses needed to be trained because the average nurse's working life was longer than previously, and contract employees could always be drafted in to fill any gaps, would be far more closely attended to than in the past. In 1960 it would be a brave hospital secretary who tried to contradict a matron's views on how many girls she wanted in her school each year.

The Treasury's view had great appeal to NHS officials. They were faced with spending money on the education of women who would play no significant part in the work of hospitals for three years, and whom the staff would hardly ever see. Loyalty is a two way process. Nor were the new nurses seen as a particularly good 'buy'. Why spend money on a graduate who after three years training did not know how to put a sling on a patients arm? In 1993/94 the Department of Health cut the numbers of commissions for student nurses by 16.15 per cent.

It was the right moment to do it. The profession was seriously demoralized and poorly led. Nursing was becoming increasingly unpopular among well-qualified applicants. The previous year, 1992 was a watershed for the NHS. It had been an election year and, scenting victory after years of Tory rule, the Labour Party set out to destroy their opponent's health reforms. Determined to halt bed closures and to prevent what they portrayed as the privatisation of the service, the Tory NHS took a tremendous beating in the left wing press. The NHS was depicted as a hell hole in which no sensible person would want to work. Little was done to correct this impression by nursing leaders who have never made any secret of their socialist leanings, and the predictions of doom became self-fulfilling. What idealistic young women would want to work in a service that was endlessly portrayed by TV, radio and the press as heartless, driven by greed and intent on forcing even old-age pensioners to pay with their life savings for medical treatment? Numbers of recruits could be expected to drop steeply.

There was a very great fall in numbers, a fall that is only just being reversed. Numbers slowly rose by 2,780 between 1995 and 1998 as commissioning was increased again to make up for theses self-inflicted losses, but there are still, according to figures from the nursing registration authorities, 8,000 fewer nurses training this year (1998) than in 1984 and the number of qualified nurses is down by 1,600 since last year. Despite £2.5 million pounds being spent on advertising and guarantees of bursaries and fees for further degrees, the NHS administration has only managed to claw back 50 per cent of the generation of nursing recruits it has lost over the past decade – a lost generation who will not be at the bedside in the coming years.

The fall in morale

In addition, word of mouth rumours were beginning to spread about the low quality of Project 2000 courses, and an even lower educational quality among applicants. Innumerate and illiterate after years of 'schooling', many candidates realized they would not be able to cope even with courses which can scarcely be described as intellectually demanding. Today, reports the Department of Education, some nurses

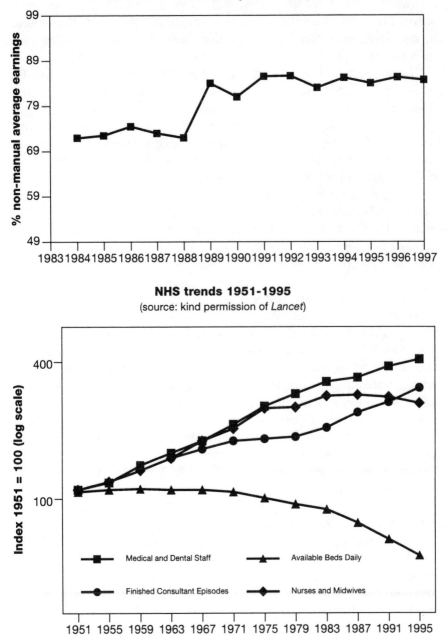

Nurses earnings during 1984 to 1997 as a proportion of all non-manual earnings

(source: *Nurses' Work: An Analysis of the UK Nursing Labour Market*, James Buchan, Ian Seccombe, Gabrielle Smith. Ashgate Publishing Ltd 1998)

NHS trends 1951-1995

(source: kind permission of *Lancet*)

Medical and Dental Staff   Available Beds Daily

Finished Consultant Episodes   Nurses and Midwives

are so ignorant of mathematics they have difficulty in calculating drug doses safely.

Nor were qualified nurses any happier. Like the students their complaints were not about pay but about a crumbling professional ethic. The profession was no longer united. A new breed of manager nurse, loyal to the NHS administration rather than nursing colleagues, was appearing.

'I was fairly happy with my salary [in 1992]' said a nurse midwife, although as a lifelong socialist she was not keen on the reforms that had been introduced by the Thatcher Government. She left, not because of money, but because there was too much work, too few nurses, and she was overseen by a nurse manager who would not attend cases even when her subordinates were working flat out for fear it would compromise her 'managerial' status.

Low pay had never stopped young women from wanting to nurse, what had fractured was the idea of professional loyalty, the psychological contract that binds members of a profession together against outsiders. Effectively broken by a divisive management and radical education reforms that mocked the values and standards of the past, nurses were no longer a profession, but a vociferous lobby group campaigning for better 'rights' and pay.

However, even if the salary of a ward sister had been raised at the time to £80,000, it is unlikely the decline could have been halted or, if so, only for a few years. High pay attracts the ambitious. Ambition would not be served by the less attractive but equally essential side of nursing, washing the helpless, comforting the senile, noticing the smell of personal neglect, feeding those who cannot feed themselves. Quite the contrary. The history of nursing since the 'reforms' of the late 1970s is of upgrading nurses' 'status' by paying them in university degrees or management posts rather than extra money. Such incentives, far from keeping the nurse at the bedside, have driven her from it. Large sums of money would only make matters worse.

This is not to say nurses should not be paid decent wages – neither writer is of the school who thinks nurses should be paid a pittance in order to keep out those who are not gentlewomen. But nursing is a vocation, a call to charity and compassion, not a job paying psychological 'danger money'. Nursing's collapse is a cultural and spiritual one, a failure of the notion of charity and compassion, not the result of failed pay bargaining rounds.

A decline in professionalism and particular loyalties

Young women who want to nurse want to join a profession, to share its ideals, to be loyal to it. Twenty years ago student nurses could do just that. They joined a hospital to which they could offer what advertising men today know as a 'brand loyalty'. You were a St Thomas', a Manchester Royal Infirmary or a Great Ormond Street trained nurse. Pay was awful, conditions hard, but you were in a family, you were at 'your' hospital doing what you wanted to do, nursing the sick from the day you started.

Today, young women are faced with spending eighteen months of their three year training on the campuses of often very minor universities. Many are discouraged, feel at sea with subjects such as sociology and psychology, wonder about the enormously tortuous and politically correct language of the tutors and sense they are being taken for something of a ride by the academic establishment. Most would prefer to nurse – to learn by practice.

This failure to recruit the next generation of students has had a devastating effect on morale among already-qualified nurses. As recruitment falls, so the amount of work nurses have to do increases, or they see their work handed over to orderlies. The key to a reform of nursing is a reform of nurse training.

Nurses are only too well aware of this. There is widespread dissatisfaction at the nature and quality of the teaching. Again in the *Nursing Times*:

> Project 2000 is about as academically thoroughgoing as the *Daily Star's* Christmas Quiz: it seeks to align the theoretical framework of nursing in a vague and minor form of sociology.

A student complains, 'If we are expected to become competent nurses after an education such as this, it's a joke'.

High dropout rates

Unsurprisingly, dropout rates from diploma courses in nursing are high. They are said to be between 15 and 20 per cent over a three-year course, and in some cases are as high as 30 per cent or even higher. But it is impossible to obtain an accurate picture. Enormous efforts are made to suppress anything which contradicts the prevailing philosophy that nurses must have degrees or diplomas. It is believed that a market survey commissioned by the Department of Health which confirmed that young women were put off nursing by the Project 2000 course was binned.

Enquiries by one of us were made at university training schools at Luton, Oxford, St George's Tooting and Manchester as to the number of nurses leaving courses. In all but one case (Manchester, where dropout rates were low) when the authorities realized the nature of the enquiry they stopped returning calls. Enquiries among student nurses on attachment to various clinics were similarly blocked on the grounds that it was 'unfair' to ask students such questions. The nursing training authorities for St George's hospital in London, one of Britain's major teaching hospitals, were repeatedly approached both by telephone and once in writing for figures, but without success. The dean of another nursing school, replying to our letter, 'regretted she was unable to supply the information requested' and suggested we contact the regional NHS executive. They had referred us to her in the first place! The reason for this Byzantine culture of secrecy is puzzling. It has been speculated that, as training places at university are sold on the NHS internal market, universities may be unwilling to reveal the extent of their failure to retain students. Whatever the reason, if there are large numbers of student nurses leaving courses it is a matter of serious public concern.

To compound this haemorrhage, the government inexplicably cut the intake of student nurses around 1993/94. While admitting this was done, the Department of Health tries to put a spin on things by emphasizing that this has been reversed by an eight per cent increase in student numbers in 1995 and a 12 per cent increase in 1996. Not only are these figures not expected to feed through until the turn of the century, it is unlikely they will prevent the fall in numbers of young women wishing to take up nursing or remaining on courses once they start to train. Worse, the Institute of Employment Studies, for example, believes that the much heralded return to nursing of many qualified nurses has now ceased to have any impact on nursing numbers.

Replacing skilled nurses with unskilled workers

The Department of Health seems instead to be wedded to a policy of replacing as many nurses as it can with unskilled labour. There is no doubt that many health managers would much prefer to see fewer expensively-trained nurses and far larger numbers of unskilled workers in the health service. Moreover, they have long had other ideas as to how they might obtain them. It may therefore have been no coincidence that managers decided to bureaucratize ignorance and low educational expectations among the large corps of unskilled non-nursing workers in the NHS in the form of National Vocational Qualifications. Starting in a small way in 1990, ward clerks, cleaners, face washers, food handlers and bed makers were paid a small retainer to train as ward orderlies. It was a brilliant coup. Preliminary training of one of these 'nurses' takes only a week or so. They are given a short induction into basic rules of hospital life, a course in mouth to mouth resuscitation to satisfy the requirements of the hospital insurance policy, and are placed on a ward. They begin work immediately, supervised by nursing staff trainers who tick little boxes showing that they are capable of carrying out a series of basic routines. Special forms and assessment schedules have been set up to check, for example, if an NVQ worker can get a patient to a lavatory and sit him at stool, see that he can clean himself and return him to the bedside.

The training, as befits any form of bureaucracy, is a series of running 'permissions' or certificates of 'competencies'. Each worker has to pass a series of small bureaucratic hoops before he is admitted to the next stage. An NVQ level three, for example, represents about two years of certification, the worker having attained the abilities of the old ward auxiliary. NVQ level one would be attained by a senior manager in the NHS. NVQs can be in any subject, in any sequence. You could obtain an NVQ for floor cleaning and then one in operating a microscope. NVQs are 'portable'. They can be carried by the worker to any part of the country. If you can wash a corpse in Manchester and have a chit to prove it, you can wash one in Abroath. What NVQs do not need is any formal education, nor does an NVQ candidate have to belong to any form of troublesome professional body. *A Guide to NVQs in Care* tells us:

> Because candidates do not have to have 'O' levels or any other qualifications in order to apply to undertake NVQ assessment, and because there are no exams, NVQs do not set up unnecessary barriers to candidates.

The idea that favouring those with formal education is discriminatory is now an extremely fashionable theory among educators.

An NVQ qualification is fast and flexible, it can be as long or as short as a candidate or his employer requires, and, most important of all, it puts the training of hospital workers in the hands of management. To avoid the charge that unskilled people are training the unskilled, the rules prescribe that only skilled people can certify the unskilled. But as the trained people themselves are now taking NVQs in training, and a huge consultative edifice run by bureaucrats has been erected to set national standards of 'training', the trainers themselves are in reality in fee to the administration. Everything can be covered. There are even NVQs in looking after the dying. The clumsy, almost vicious language of the bureaucrat even intrudes on this, that most private and individual of all exchanges of charity between nurse and patient:

> NC3. Sub-section Support individuals and others through the process of dying. NC3.1 Support individuals their partners relatives and friends in their initial adjustment to learning of the individuals imminent death. – sic. (Ref National Occupational Standards upon which NVQs are based)

How NVQs might progress in the NHS can be seen from the following. By 1996, of the 332,660 nursing, midwifery and health visiting staff working in the NHS, one quarter (83,650) were unqualified. It is this core of workers and their successors whom management would like to see holding NVQs. The more NVQs there are, the more direct control there is over patient care by management.

One of the key targets is the 11 per cent of this total, so-called 'support workers' and health care assistants. These two grades have taken the place of the old state-enrolled nurses on the wards. Prior to the education reforms of Salmon and Project 2000, women with limited education could, after a two-year simplified nursing course, register as state-enrolled nurses. They were excellent nurses, highly competent and the mainstay of many wards. But events overtook them. Nursing leaders, obsessed with the idea of image and status, started to phase them out.

From 1985, unless they were prepared to undertake a further two years' training – often beyond their abilities and at their own cost – they were effectively defrocked to health-care assistants. Having therefore lost their professional status they now fell under the hand of management. Encouraged to take NVQs they were, therefore, the first nurses to be detached from the profession. As the older generation of these women retires, management is replacing them with staff even more directly under their control.

For example, a major teaching hospital recently advertised for 'support staff', cleaners, ward orderlies, nursing auxiliaries. Ninety people applied and after a simple literacy test, 45 were accepted. Most had previous jobs ranging from a sales assistant to a bank clerk. Most were over 22 years of age. They were offered a year's post at £10,000 a year plus £1,000 training allowance.

What is concealed is the degree of surrender the acceptance of these qualifications might mean for the nursing profession proper. NVQs are no longer confined to non-nursing staff. Very slowly health authorities are beginning to introduce the idea of NVQs that run in tandem with professional qualifications. You might, for example, be a senior laboratory research worker with a PhD, but that would not stop your employers asking you to take an NVQ in, say, laboratory safety or glassware work. Operating room technicians have their own NVQs. How long will it be before senior nursing theatre sisters are encouraged to obtain them as well in 'the interests of upgrading their practical skills' or as part of a 'continuing education process'?

Alternative qualifications such as these set a dangerous precedent. To be an operating theatre technician you do not have to be a nurse. How long will it be before a ward sister does not have to be a nurse? An NVQ level four, for example, (which in another profession, say law, would make you the equivalent of a solicitor, but without obligatory education) would, said one senior nurse educator, pose a serious threat to the nursing profession.

A decline in professional autonomy
However reasonable and logical such qualifications look on the surface, once they are accepted a decline in professional autonomy is inevitable. NVQs open the way to direct control of patient treatment by bureaucrats. Bureaucrats deny this, pointing out that all NVQs are tested by professionals in their field, not by them. For example, nurses certify health-care assistants, lawyers law clerks, research workers laboratory staff, and so on. Bureaucrats claim that all they do is merely to administer what is considered 'best practice' by the professions. In reality, however, it allows them to impose rigid, unalterable codes of practice on the lower echelons of the professions. The practice of nursing or medicine then becomes merely a bureaucratic tool, a device directed at the advancement of administrators not the good of the patient.

This form of management is now settling like a shroud not only over industry but over health systems all over the western world, anywhere where consumerism has taken hold. America leads the way with managed care in which treatments (culled from a consensus of medical and nursing opinion) are standardized by bureaucrats and then imposed on nurses and doctors. The result is rule by a frightening cabal of managers and lawyers, a legalistic, defensive form of medicine which at best demeans, at worst kills. A British nurse writing in the *Nursing Times* describes her experience of working in a US hospital. She describes a world of suspicion and bad faith. 'The system was rigid and ritualistic with no room for error ... Every mistake we made was entered into our files for consideration at the performance-related pay review.' Eventually, as in any system based on suspicion instead of trust, disaster struck. The nurse became involved in an inquiry. Although exonerated, she was forced to endure a year of hell defending herself. And bureaucracy still went in pursuit. She was fined US$750 by the Department of Professional Regulation for mistakenly writing 10pm instead of 9.15pm on a report.

Such an episode should come as no surprise. Both in the US and the UK, nurses have indeed become what their leaders promised in the early 1970s: corporate executives in a fast turnover industry called Health Care. Like all industries it has been rationalised and 'downsized'. Beds have been cut by 50 per cent. The new nurse with her Diploma in Nursing Studies is expected to hurry patients in and out of the remaining beds like passengers on and off a bus. Patients who once would arrive in hospital for a relatively major operation could expect to spend ten days on the ward. Now even after a heart operation a stay of three days is quite normal. Strangers arrive, are processed, repaired and then discharged. Faces no longer mean anything. Relatives are just a blur of anxious people visiting and leaving.

Impersonalisation
For this to be possible nurses have become administrators. Each shift has to spend at least an hour filling in management protocols on the ward computer. Clerical staff make constant demands on the senior nursing staff for information about ward activities. Clipboard-wielding clerks lurk on the wards ticking little boxes for time and motion studies. Meetings can last for hours, often over the most bizarre and Kafkaesque decisions. Everywhere the idea of the personal nurse and a professional ladder of responsibility is in retreat. According to a senior sister on a major burns unit of a London teaching hospital where every minute wasted on administration is time lost on attending to those in pain and desperately ill: 'We had to devote all our ingenuity to find a way of avoiding naming a nurse in charge, so we could keep our ward sister

without the managers noticing. It took us many hours of anxious form filling.' She showed me shelves filled with boxes of unread protocols, painfully put together by the nursing and medical staff, only to be ignored by management.

As with any modern corporation, there is a huge reliance on machines. This is particularly applicable to intensive care units where the patient may arrive unconscious, be repaired and returned to his ward without ever meeting those who have looked after him. A wall of technology often separates the patient from his nurse. He cannot move because he is paralysed by drugs. He cannot speak because a tube has been inserted in his windpipe, he cannot think because his brain function has been arrested by powerful gases. As the patient sinks further and further into a web of machines, it is more and more difficult to distinguish between him and the machines that are keeping him alive. Nurses fear that eventually patients will become an interchangeable part of the machine, to be discarded as they fail.

Neglecting the sick, interfering with the healthy

In a final, logical step away from patients, vast hierarchies of health educators, health visitors and other preventioneers outside the hospital are draining nurses from the bedside. Their aim is not to nurse the sick but to gain licensing power over the healthy. Health visitors would like to be able to issue 'permission' for women to look after their children. Health educators would like to 'permit' people to teach or learn how to prevent illness. Illustrative of this is the experience of one of the authors who, while training to be a district nurse in 1987, was forbidden by her tutors, as a matter of formal teaching, to make cups of tea or make the beds of elderly people at home. District nurses are administrative directors, permission givers. They licence care at home. Nursing is to be done by orderlies. Status for the new 'nursing' hierarchy is more important than compassion.

Surprisingly, nurses have no language for dealing with this stark dilemma. Thirty years of misdirected 'reform' and the vain pursuit of status have left the leaders of the profession morally impoverished. It is no accident that modern nurses' leaders have no language to describe the plight of their profession. Twenty years as corporate executives have stripped them of English. Nursing leaders talk about the conflict between humanity and technology, and demand that there should be 'reflective spaces' for nurses, more 'support networks' and more postgraduate education. But such phrases are the false coin of consumerism and marketing, a language that has arisen from the very nature of this dehumanizing technology.

There is, however, a strong feeling among working nurses who face these problems daily, that reform is urgently needed. But very few have any idea of which direction the reforms should take. There have been frequent calls for the return of the Matron, of nurses' uniforms and the old type of ward training. On occasions the calls have become so vociferous that token matrons have been appointed by some health authorities, but they are only exercises in public relations. Their real controllers are overweening administrations. The danger is that not only will the public believe them, but so will their creators, that all that is necessary to reform nursing is to change the nurses' image. This has been shown to be a house built on sand.

Reform has to go deeper than that. And it is urgent. Just ahead stands the 'health care professional', a grey technician in 'gender neutral fatigues' with a bogus vocabulary of 'care', a figure people will come to fear as much as the undertaker or the prison warder. This new, sanitized Sarah Gamp, with a PhD in health studies, a diploma in finance management and NVQs in the new science of thanatology (patient care/agreed protocols of dying) will come to haunt us by 2020.

A return to charity

What can nurses do? Nursing's aim must be to restore the old values of love and charity at the bedside. A traditionally-trained nurse recalls how she was taught. 'Anybody we nursed we had to think of as our own mother or father, brother or sister.' This was not a bureaucratic approach. Nursing is a vocation, a giving of one's self to the patient. The clerk – the NVQ-trained floor assistant – does not give anything, he merely fulfils a series of functions in return for pay. Nursing, although it uses science and technology, is not based on it.

The very first aim of the nursing reformer, therefore, must be the return of the student nurse to the bedside, not as an observer, but as a member of staff, owing her loyalty to a hospital, a place where the sick are treated, not to a distant campus. The idea that nursing is an academic discipline taught at university may sound attractive and 'status enhancing' but it is foolish. It is based on the idea that science is better than compassion. Theoretical modules in psychology and women's studies does not make a good nurse. Distancing the nurse from the bedside only decreases her understanding of the sick.

It also distances her from her colleagues. Readers may be surprised at one of the central tenets of the new science of nursing, that a nurse does not take orders from a doctor. She is a professional in her own right. Horror is expressed at the idea that doctors once set nurses' exams and ran their lectures. Young nurses are told that the old Nightingale nurses nursed strictly according to what they were told by doctors, not because they understood what they were doing.

This is insulting to generations of perceptive and dedicated Nightingale nurses. Even more so when we consider what can happen today.

> On the day she [a 91-year-old lady who had had pneumonia] was discharged the hospital sent her home by ambulance with only a thin night dress and a blanket over her knees. It was February and very cold. The hospital had put her dressing gown in a bag. The staff in the home my mother stayed in said she had urine burns and ... were disgusted that a patient should be allowed to get into this state in a hospital. (*Observer*, 1997)

Only in a world that teaches that science and status go hand in hand could such things happen. Worse, creating an academic science of nursing means that the young, newly-qualified nurse is already half persuaded when she enters hospital that science and technology are admirable things. She becomes instantly complicity in an insane progress. Patients do not need 'progress', they need to understand they are human beings, that one day they will die. People who do not accept death are not human. Nursing is about teaching people to be human.

Secondly, nurses should not entertain the idea that an NVQ qualification is in any way equal to, or a substitute for being a nurse, and therefore a member of an independent profession. Just as government only works well if the executive, the judiciary and parliamentarians all pursue slightly different aims, so a hospital is only safe if doctors, nurses and managers are to some extent at each others' throats. Handing over the training of a large part of the hospital staff to the administration – even with token nurses running it – creates an enormous power imbalance in this finely-balanced triumvirate, and is highly dangerous.

And back into uniform

The third reform is the restoration of a distinctive professional uniform for nurses. Many nurses have done away with their uniforms under the mistaken impression that they were outdated and anti-feminist. One patient described to me how she had a baby delivered in a London teaching hospital by a nurse in street clothes wearing a huge pair of Doc Martens. While this has its comic aspects it is political suicide for nurses to identify themselves with an administration which is bent on wiping them out by wearing the same clothes. Nurses need to emphasize the fact that they are different and separate. As with policemen or airline pilots, the public look to uniforms and rank to satisfy their wish to be in the hands of an ordered, separate profession. This reform is no mere detail, but an important psychological weapon in the struggle that nurses are going to have to wage with the new technology. Putting on her uniform to go to work should be seen as a nurse's assertion of the independence of her profession, a challenge alike to the machines and to their administrative minders.

There are some hopeful signs. To its credit, the General Nursing Council, although broadly sympathetic to the idea of adding several more layers of bureaucracy to our hospitals, has refused to entertain the idea that NVQs should be registered as nurses. It is vital that this step is never taken. Professions have moral rules, ideals of right and wrong which are not easily certified by bureaucrats. They have a vision of what society ought to be like, and ideals of behaviour that can appear to be absurdly out of date. Doctors, for example, opposed abortion for centuries, although it was an ideal form of population control. It is only now, with one in five of our children being killed before birth, that we can see how right they were to take such a reactionary stand. Nurses feel, but are not quite sure, that there is something profoundly wrong with the modern hospital. It is fast becoming a bureaucratic engine that churns out repaired people. But many of them are people who are profoundly damaged, both spiritually and mentally.

Bureaucrats will always colonize those spaces which the professions have left unfilled. In the case of nursing, the unfilled space has been a moral and ethical one. Nurses have to re-occupy this ground. It is time they asked their leaders to leave. And it is time for a break with what has become an occupying power in the NHS, an overweening management. Nurses need to take back their hospitals, their uniforms and their training.

Reopening the old nursing schools

Revolutions need a signal, a battle colour run up the mast. In 1996, Florence Nightingale's Nurses' School at St Thomas' Hospital, London shut its doors to its last traditionally-trained nurses. This great school which had offered young women the very latest and best in the practice of nursing for 136 years would now move to a lay university outside the hospital. The move signalled a change in loyalty, from the bedside to the lecture hall, from patient to theory. Student nurses would still visit the hospital but they would no longer be truly part of it.

Coming as it did long after virtually every other traditional nursing school had closed its doors, the closure, a hugely publicised event, was a calculated afterthought. Had it been announced when Project 2000 was born that schools like St Thomas would close, there would have been an outcry. Instead, to spin doctors' pronouncements about new dimensions in nursing care, nurses and the public were presented with a *fait accompli*. A great tradition in British nursing was now over, we the public could like it or lump it.

But neither the public, nor the young women who would have flocked into our nursing schools had they been left as they were, will lump 'reforms' that have wrecked nursing. Sooner or later they will have to be set aside. St Thomas' nursing school, along with hundreds of other training schools across the country, will have to reopen. It is not a matter of choice, but of necessity. Without nurses the NHS will falter, then collapse. Just as St Thomas' was a symbol of reform 100 years ago, so it is today. Every day its famous nursing school remains closed, we the public will know that another day has passed with the government doing nothing about a coming catastrophe, one that will affect all of us. Let them remember we have our remedy at the polls.

2

Closing time in the gardens of the West

The state of higher education

Jeffrey Richards

The purpose of a university was the cultivation of intellect

In a celebrated *Horizon* editorial in 1949, Cyril Connolly declared that it was 'closing time in the gardens of the West' and presciently predicted the crisis that was to overtake the Western liberal intellectual tradition in the 1960s when the long-established 'givens' of the culture – authority, truth, objectivity and judgement – were rejected wholesale. This had the effect of overturning a centuries-old view of universities and their role.

That established view was succinctly defined by John Henry Newman in his classic work *The Idea of a University*, published in 1873 but containing lectures he had been delivering over the previous 20 years. He enunciated a series of truths that were universally acknowledged both in Britain and America until at least the 1960s. The University was a community of scholars who 'learnt to respect, to consult, to aid each other' and thus create 'a pure and clear atmosphere of thought' within which the student comes to gain a liberal education, to study a variety of subjects under the guidance of the scholars. The student learns above all 'a habit of mind ... which lasts through life, of which the attributes are freedom, equitableness, calmness, moderation and wisdom'. The student pursues the truth, by which Newman meant objective knowledge. 'Knowledge is ... its own end ... its own reward', he argued, calling it a view that has 'ever been the common judgement of philosophers and the ordinary feeling of mankind'.

However, the end of a liberal education was not mere knowledge and learning, but thought and reason exercised upon knowledge, 'the cultivation of the intellect ... an end which may reasonably be pursued for its own sake'. A liberal education produced a gentleman: 'It is well to be a gentleman, it is well to have a cultivated intellect, a delicate taste, a candid, equitable, dispassionate mind, a noble and courteous bearing in the conduct of life'. Newman does not rule out the study of useful skills such as medicine and law which may benefit society, but utility is secondary to the main purpose of a university – the training of the mind and the character: 'A cultivated intellect, because it is good in itself, brings with it a power and a grace to every work and occupation which it undertakes, and enables us to be more useful, and to a greater number'.[1]

Universities produced a trained, intellectual, gentlemanly elite

If a practical end must be assigned to a university education, then, according to Newman, it was training good members of society.

> It aims at raising the intellectual tone of a society, at cultivating the public mind, at purifying the national taste, at supplying true principles to popular enthusiasm and fixed aims to popular aspirations, at giving enlargement and sobriety to the ideas of the age, at facilitating the exercise of political power, and refining the intercourse of private life.[2]

In short, universities are to produce a trained, intellectual, gentlemanly elite whose aim is not their own enrichment but, like Plato's Guardians, to guide, instruct and inspire society.

Knowledge still for its own sake in newer universities in the 1950s

With but few qualifications, this was still the view that was being expressed in 1951 by Bruce Truscot in *Red Brick University* in which he wrote of a world in which 'Oxbridge' had been joined by the 'civic' or 'red brick' universities during the first quarter of the twentieth century (Manchester, Birmingham, Sheffield, Leeds, Bristol, Reading). 'A university' he wrote, 'is a corporation or society which devotes itself to the search after knowledge for the sake of its intrinsic value'. The twin aims of the university were research (the advancement of knowledge) and teaching (the dissemination of knowledge). He believed his ideal university could be maintained and promoted by precept, by relating scholarship to character and leadership, and by advancing the 'ideal of service', the equivalent of Newman's ideal of good citizenship.[3]

Still 'fountains of spiritual leadership' in 1964

There was another extension of the system in the 1960s, in the wake of the Robbins Report, when 'Oxbridge' and the 'red brick' universities were joined by the 'plate glass' or 'new' universities, usually on greenfield sites outside old cathedral or county towns (Lancaster, York, East Anglia, Kent, Warwick, Stirling, etc). Lord Robbins was aware of the dangers attached to expansion, but he defended the old concept of the university in a speech to a conference of European Rectors and Vice-Chancellors at Göttingen in 1964. He argued for the expansion of the university system to accommodate all those qualified to undertake such an education and not just the privileged few. But he underlined the importance of the 'contribution to the progress and texture of civilization which our universities have to make, not only as centres of training, but also as centres of thought and learning'. It was more than ever important, he thought, to enable 'the life of the spirit' to flourish and to maintain universities as 'fountains of ideas and spiritual leadership', so that by the ethos and manner in which teaching was carried out, intellectual habits and moral assumptions appropriate to the membership of a free society should be instilled – the values of critical objectivity, fairness and humanity.[4]

Those charged with the implementation of such ideals were the academics. The role and values of the academic had largely survived the transformation in their nature in the mid-nineteenth century from Oxbridge clergymen to academic professionals. Harold Perkin writes in his study of the rise of the professional society:

> Transformed from without by the pressure of largely middle-class opinion ... the two universities were transformed in a generation from clerical-run seminars for the Anglican clergy and finishing schools for leisured gentlemen into professionalized institutions. They were operated by career dons for the sons of the landed and professional classes preparing for careers in the public service, including politics, the home and Indian Civil Services, colonial government and the liberal professions.[5]

But the values they taught were the agreed values of public service – the manifestation of a gentlemanliness which was not merely a matter of birth but of value systems and mindsets inculcated as part of the character-training received at school and university.

The academic today – the job looks the same but the values have changed

In its externals, the job of the academic remains much the same as it was in the nineteenth century. The academic does research which involves primary investigation and experimentation, writing books and papers, attending and organizing conferences, refereeing and reviewing books and articles, editing scholarly series and journals, delivering lectures to outside bodies and organizations, and generally keeping up with the work in his field. The academic teaches at the undergraduate and postgraduate level and this involves preparing and delivering courses of lectures, small group teaching, setting and marking essays and exercises of various kinds, setting, marking and supervising examinations, writing references, supervising dissertations and generally advising students at all levels about their work. But if one looks deeper, there is no longer any agreement about the values to be instilled or, indeed, about whether any values should be instilled at all.

The academic's job assailed by anarchic Romanticism

At one level this is because academics are no longer *in loco parentis*. When the age of majority was lowered to 18 in 1969 students became legally adults and academics ceased to be surrogate parents with parental responsibility. But it went much deeper than that. The universities, like every other institution, were transformed by the cultural revolution of the 1960s. The best interpretation of the 1960s I know is that of Bernice Martin, who sees that decade as the latest manifestation of Romanticism and, as such, parallel to the intellectual and cultural upheavals of the late eighteenth and early nineteenth centuries. She argues that Romanticism seeks to destroy boundaries, to reject conventions, to undermine structures and universalize the descent into the abyss and the ascent into the infinite. The matrix of this Romanticism was material prosperity, which released people from the immediate disciplines of survival and concentrated their attention on their expressive needs – self-discovery, self-fulfilment, self-expression, sensation. It is a doctrine which is quintessentially individualist and focused on the self rather than on communal needs and social obligations.

1960s Romantics reacted against a world that was highly structured, traditional and conventional, that was in essence still Victorian. In its place they advocated a culture of liminality, in which the outsider, the rebel and the deviant were heroes, spontaneity was everything and rules, restrictions, conventions and traditions in art, in thought and in life were ditched. This tide of romantic individualism engulfed the universities in Britain, Continental Europe and the United States, where opposition to the Vietnam War provided an excuse for taking the rebellion to the streets.[6]

The eclipse of the gentlemanly ethic

Culturally one of the most significant developments of the 1960s was the eclipse of the gentlemanly ethic which had been central to British and American culture for a century.[7] Gentlemanliness was declared outdated, patronizing and class-based. The whole thrust of popular culture in the 1960s and since has constituted a massive rejection of the old value systems. So gentleman heroes as cultural role models like Ronald Colman, Leslie Howard and Gary Cooper were replaced with the likes of Sylvester Stallone, Charles Bronson and Arnold Schwarzenegger, violent, inarticulate, neanderthal thugs. The culture became increasingly self-obsessed, individualistic, egalitarian and proletarian. In the face of this, it became impossible for the universities, even if they still wished to, to turn out gentlemen or, indeed, ladies. Feminism repudiated the concept of the lady as patronizing, prescriptive and paternalist. Elitism and paternalism, the underlying principles of the Newmanian ideal, became dirty words.

The effect on teaching, research, the curriculum: the rejection of character formation

As Martin points out, all of this had a far-reaching effect on the nature of universities, on the curriculum, on the objectives of teaching and on the roles and attitudes of academics. In all the expressive professions (religion, teaching, social work, medicine), there was a growth of egalitarianism and informality, a rejection of hierarchy, a repudiation of the idea of character-training, even of the very idea of professional status. In many universities there were bids to eliminate the distinctions between teachers and taught, to scrap assessment, to abolish staff common rooms and dining rooms. There was a move to abolish boundaries between subject areas, between high culture and mass culture. Radical academics rejected as undesirable and unattainable the old scholarly virtues of selectivity, impartiality, objectivity, critical judgement and the pursuit of truth, and instead promoted subjectivity,

41

cultural relativity, relevance and absolute identification and emotional involvement with one's subject.

A new academic elite emerged both in Britain and America, steeped in and promoting the new values. There occurred what Christopher Lasch has dubbed 'a revolt of the elites', which he sees as the mirror image of Ortega y Gasset's revolt of the masses. In Ortega's analysis, the elite maintained the values of civilization; mass man rejected them. Mass Man rejected authority, had no sense of history or duty, lived unthinkingly for the self and the future, and had a deadly hatred of all that were not like himself. These, Lasch argues, are now the values of the academic elite. They regard the mass as 'incorrigibly racist, sexist, provincial and xenophobic' and so opt out of the real world and into their ivory towers, the very idea of service and participation in society anathema.[8]

The rejection of Western culture

Within their ivory towers they divide up into a host of warring tribes. Postmodernity has spawned a bewildering variety of sects: structuralists, post-structuralists, deconstructionists, new historicists, feminists, Lacanians, Freudians, Saussurians, Althusserians, Foucauldians. As Kenneth Minogue has written,

> The adoption of a style of thought or special vocabulary is the common distinguishing mark of an academic tribe. Such tribes often treat their opponents with unfraternal scorn and watch nervously for heresy within their own ranks.[9]

It is a far cry from the Newmanian community of scholars respecting, consulting and aiding one another.

> What these tribes share is a rejection of Western civilization as an organized form of domination designed to enforce conformity to bourgeois values and to keep the victims of patriarchal oppression – women, children, homosexuals, people of colour – in a permanent state of oppression.[10]

A hatred of the work of dead white European males (dwems for short) underlies many of the new disciplines which have arisen, particularly in the social sciences, to dominate the academic discourse.

Sociology

Sociology was the key subject of the 1960s, its aim to document, analyze and demystify social structures, to propose methodologies and theories, and to explain and interpret social patterns. At its best, as in works like Bernice Martin's *A Sociology of Contemporary Cultural Change*, it has played a vital and shaping role in historical interpretation. At its worst, sociology is flabby flannel and windy waffle, given to saying things that are blindingly obvious in language no-one can understand. Too much of it is airy speculation, unencumbered by fact or evidence. Sociologists are great advocates of theory and much theory consists of repeating mantra-like the *aperçus* of Continental gurus as if they were gospel. The problem is that some sociologists are at heart worshippers. They want creeds, prophets, dogmas, incantations. The death of God at the end of the nineteenth century and of Karl Marx at the end of the twentieth have left them seeking new prophets with new revelations. They find them in the likes of Habermas, Beck and Bauman, Althusser, Foucault and Baudrillard, names uttered with the uncritical reverence which in the past was accorded to Isaiah and St Paul. They speak a special mandarin language, impenetrable to outsiders, and resemble nothing so much as medieval theologians constructing hierarchies of the cherubim and the seraphim. All of this flouts the fundamental directive enunciated by Umberto Eco, 'accessibility is a moral duty for academics'. Eco practised what he preached by writing best-selling novels and regular newspaper columns along with his academic monographs. It is not uncommon in Italy, France or Germany for leading academics to communicate with the wider public through the mass media. In Britain this is practised by the heroic few but looked upon with suspicion by the intellectually snobbish and defensively exclusive many, who mistrust anything that the man in the street can understand. But academics should above all communicate not just with each other but with the wider world. To fail in this is surely a dereliction of duty.

Women's Studies
Women's Studies and the whole concept of gender in history has added a vital new dimension to our understanding of both the past and the present. I for one would not be without this new and immensely enriching area of scholarship. At its best, Women's Studies has rescued the neglected experiences and life histories of half the population, providing new insights and perspectives. At its worst, however, it is likely to consist of covens of shrill harridans in boiler suits, sitting around slagging off men and uncritically parroting slogans –

'patriarchal oppression'; 'phallocratic view of the universe'; 'all men are rapists', which is as fatuous and indefensible a proposition as to say that all women are sluts.

This approach is group therapy and not scholarship in any way that I understand the term, unless it is the Oprah Winfrey school of academic investigation.

There have been several unfortunate by-products of Women's Studies. One is the exclusivism – the deplorable idea that women alone should study their subject and men should be excluded, as scandalous a denial of academic freedom as the actions of those benighted Oxford dons of the 1920s who drove women from their lectures by cruelty and sarcasm. Then there is victimology. This is the new cultural 'given' – that all women, all ethnic minorities, the disabled and so forth, are all victims of that embodiment of all evil: white, middle-class, male patriarchal society. It has produced what Robert Hughes has dubbed 'the culture of complaint', in which everyone is a victim and no-one takes responsibility for anything.[11] But this is a 'goodies' and 'baddies' view of history, a crutch for the intellectually lazy, an approach that went out before Sellar and Yeatman satirized it in *1066 and All That*.

Cultural Studies

Finally, what Sociology was for the 1960s, Cultural Studies has become for the 1990s. It started out dominated by Marxism as refined by Gramsci and applied to culture. But Marxism, which was for several generations the opium of the intelligentsia, has been substantially discredited in theory and in practice. It is demonstrably not the case that people are primarily economic units and are engaged in permanent class war. Nationalism and religious fundamentalism have proved at least as potent as class war in inspiring people. To replace Marx, new gurus have arisen, some of whom are now being revealed not so much as philosophers, but as autobiographers, with a particular line in special pleading. Michel Foucault's influential work on prisons, madness and sexuality, all featuring the individual oppressed by the power structures of the state, is at heart pure and uncritical autobiography, universalized as theory. Paul De Man developed the theory of deconstructionism by which it is proposed that nothing means anything and everything is merely a variety of competing discourses. This was just the kind of theory to appeal to a generation who have rejected the fundamental liberal humanist belief in the power of great literature and art to exert a civilizing influence. But De Man also turns out to be an

44

autobiographer, covering up by a theory of linguistic meaninglessness his past as a Nazi collaborator in occupied Belgium.

Relativism

The central theme of Cultural Studies is relativism, the view that there is no difference of value between works of art, between, say, a Doris Day song and an Elgar symphony, between a picture postcard and the Sistine Chapel ceiling. Popular culture should certainly be analyzed. Advertizing slogans, soap operas, rock music, cartoons are perfectly legitimate objects of study. But this does not make them equal in value to great art. By no sensible definition of art could the collected works of Jackie Collins be regarded as on a par with those of Jane Austen. Yet this is the logic of the relativist position. It is the product of a total failure of nerve, a refusal to arrive at and defend judgements, in short, intellectual cowardice. Harold Bloom, a robust defender of the canon, is pessimistic:

> Finding myself now surrounded by professors of hip-hop; by clones of Gallic-Germanic theory; by ideologues of gender and of various sexual persuasions; by multi-culturalisms unlimited, I realize that the Balkanization of literary studies is irreversible.[12]

He predicts the replacement before long of university literature departments by departments of cultural studies.

Literature, as it was understood up to the 1970s and 1980s, emerged as a basic university and school subject in the period 1880-1920. It was in part a product of the intelligentsia's fear of the brutalizing, dehumanizing and philistinizing effects of industrial society on the populace at large. The study of great literature was to be the key to their liberation from this state of affairs.

The rejection of the past

However, the pervasive influence of 'political correctness' upon cultural studies means that virtually all pre-twentieth century literature is now dismissed as racist, sexist, bourgeois, authoritarian, and, as such, unworthy of study or at best to be examined simply for the purposes of condemnation. There could be no better example of what E P Thompson memorably called 'the enormous condescension of posterity', the arrogant assumption that we in the late twentieth century have a monopoly of all wisdom and that all who went before were benighted, ignorant, or straightforwardly wicked. But 'the past is a foreign country'. Scholars should seek to understand and explain it and not merely condemn.

Then, there is the pernicious influence of 'relevance'. Ageing 1960s trendies appear regularly on television to tell us that *Eastenders* is more important than Shakespeare because 'the kids can relate to it'. Shakespeare is no longer relevant because he was white, male, middle-class, middle-aged and used long words. It might just as well be argued that he should not be studied because he was bald and came from Stratford. The enduring relevance of the study of great literature lies in its ability to hone the critical faculties, to enlarge the spirit, to awaken a love of language, to understand the past, to interpret universal human experience and eternal emotional and spiritual truths. For that one goes to great literature and whether it derives from Ancient Greece, sixteenth-century Florence or nineteenth-century England is comparatively unimportant.

The revolt of the elites has not been total. It is more advanced in American than in British universities, it is more influential in the social sciences and the humanities than in the sciences. There remain everywhere embattled groups of Newmanians who cling to the pristine view of the university, but they are an endangered species. For they are fighting not just the abandonment of the old academic virtues, but the rise to prominence of a purely utilitarian view of the university.

The new training ethos
As early as 1973, Sir Charles Carter, founding Vice-Chancellor of Lancaster University, was writing:

> We have damaged the true cause of civilization and culture by trying to convince people that universities are "good business" and that education has a yield as good as that of a jam factory.[13]

Lord Annan wrote in 1975:

> The dons do not regard themselves as vocational teachers. They regard themselves as dedicated to the task of discovering new knowledge and redrawing the map of existing knowledge.[14]

But they were beginning to sound like voices from a previous age. The new egalitarian tone of society required a new rationale for universities and that was the idea of training people for specific jobs, precisely the utilitarian rationale that Newman had rejected.

The change in the nature of universities and of the role of academics within them was completed by the application to the system of the model of the free market – the Thatcherization of the universities in the 1980s. This involved the transformation of universities from communities of scholars into businesses, with the emphasis laid on vocational training, the inculcation of marketable skills, the reduction in state funding and the encouragement of private financing, and the importation of structures from America geared to facilitating customer choice. The wholesale upgrading of the polytechnics to university status signalled the direction of government higher education policy.

Robert Nisbet has suggested that the process of commercialization began in America in the 1950s when universities which had previously shared the Newmanian ideal were overtaken by the higher capitalism, first in the natural sciences, then the social sciences and, finally, the humanities. This led to the rise of the 'new men of power' – academic capitalists and professional entrepreneurs. So academics began to be appointed not for their abilities in teaching or research but for their money-raising and managerial capacities. Such figures often stood outside the traditional structures of the university, developing semi-autonomous fiefdoms, externally-funded units that spearheaded the commodification of research.[15]

This has now begun to happen in Britain where – inconceivable a generation ago – it is possible to hear people referring to the university as 'the business' and students as 'the product'.

History

My own subject, history, teaches many useful skills: information gathering, problem solving, public presentation of arguments and assessments. But that should be secondary to the broader objective of discovering how we were and how we got to where we are. It is not my purpose to turn out tunnel-visioned computer operators concerned only about where their next Porsche is coming from. I seek to awaken in my students an open-minded, broad-visioned humanity, informed by a love of learning, a love of ideas, a love of books, a love of argument and debate. An educated population is one of the glories of a civilized country and that is the end and objective of university education. It should be available to everyone who is equipped to benefit from it and it should be based on full student grants and generous state funding.

Economic plus cultural changes threaten the character of the British university

However, a combination of chronic and persistent under-funding, the adoption of a commercial ethos and self-indulgent intellectual faddishness means that what used to be a community of scholars, staff and students, engaged upon a common intellectual pursuit of intrinsic interest, value and coherence, is steadily being turned into a series of shambolic academic supermarkets in which student customers – customers, indeed – load their trolleys haphazardly from the pick'n'mix shelves with cheap, nasty, flimsy modularized products lacking in intellectual fibre and spiritual nourishment. Modularization, semesterization, privatisation, the new structural dogmas, can be summed up in one word – abomination. They will mean the end of everything that is distinctive about the British university system – classified degrees, small group teaching, the principle of intellectual maturation.

Agendas and balance sheets

Commercialization has also called into being a new tier of 'senior management'. Administration was always an element of university life. Bruce Truscot recognized it when he wrote in *Red Brick University*:

> During term, a part of the working week … is devoted either to normal meetings or to such special duties as attendance at committees for filling chairs, library committees, departmental meetings and so on. But there are two abuses of the system. First, committees … are as a rule too numerous, too large and too frequent in their meetings … Secondly, the well-known tendency to overwork the willing horse is nowhere more observable than here. The few people who are clearly fitted for committee work … are elected to committee after committee, until for half their time, they are serving tables, their term-life is spent between lecture room and committee room, and they come home at night unfit for anything but relaxation.[16]

But there are senior academics nowadays who never see the inside of a lecture-room. They are mere managers and their imaginative inner life consists entirely of drawing up agendas and balance sheets and compiling minutes. The caricatured business image of the 'good meeting', whole and contained unto itself, is inexorably creeping into university life.

This is in part the consequence of profound changes in the universities, in particular the introduction of the principle of accountability. It is perfectly right and proper that, as the recipients of public money, the universities should be subject to outside assessment. But in the space of a few years we have moved from a position of total unaccountability to one in which assessment, internal and external, has become a non-stop, year-round, twenty-four hours a day business. Academics are drowning in the alphabet soup of investigatory procedures. The Research Assessment Exercise (RAE) and Teaching Quality Audit (TQA) are only the twin peaks of a mountain of paperwork that is being demanded – mission statements, self-assessment, staff appraisals, course rationales, student questionnaires, budget plans. No sooner has one of these exercises ended than another is launched. It is the bureaucratic equivalent of painting the Forth Bridge, and it has called into being academics whose main job is to move round this mountain of paperwork.

Unionisation

The changes in the universities have completed the radicalisation of the profession which began in the 1960s. On the day in 1989 when it authorized the boycott by academics of student examinations, I resigned my membership of the Association of University Teachers (AUT). In retrospect I should have resigned several years earlier when the AUT affiliated to the Trades Union Congress and was transformed from the professional association, dedicated to the maintenance of standards, which I had joined 20 years earlier, into a trade union. Unionisation confirmed the injection into university life of the wholly alien model of industrial relations, with 'workers' (academics) and 'management' (administration) at daggers-drawn, and the hapless students held to ransom and their future careers put in jeopardy. It is alien because each teacher forms an individual pedagogical relationship with his students, which means that to refuse to set and mark their examinations is unthinkable. It is a denial of everything the dedicated teacher stands for. For university teaching, like school teaching, is not product management. It is a sacred vocation in which – to take the example of my own discipline – staff and students alike are charged with tending the flame of Clio, the muse of history, and keeping it burning by engaging in the common pursuit of knowledge and truth, explanation and understanding.

The AUT's policy was not only morally indefensible, it was tactically misguided. For there is no public sympathy for academics, largely because of the myth of 'long holidays'. It is time this myth was exploded. The majority of academics work not only during the day but in the evenings and at weekends. The vacations are spent not in the fleshpots of Bermuda or Torremolinos but in libraries and archives, preparing lectures, keeping up with new material, writing books and articles, undertaking research trips, with the aim of extending the sum of human knowledge. The total lack of recognition of this work by government and public alike, has brought deep demoralization in the profession, an increase in the incidence of stress-related illness and, in a handful of cases, suicide.

Universities bankrupt by 2005

The strain of trying to maintain a viable university system in the face of what appears to be a policy of 'death by a thousand cuts' has deepened a sense of despair and desperation in the profession. The result of progressive year-on-year funding cuts in real terms has led the Committee of Vice-Chancellors and Principals (CVCP) to predict that most universities will be bankrupt by 2005. For years, pay rises for academics have been derisory and this has accelerated the long-term erosion of status and remuneration in the profession. This, coupled with the constant reductions in funding, has also undermined job satisfaction and academics are faced with a situation in which many universities are forcing academics into early retirement, abandoning courses for lack of money to sustain them and, most seriously, cutting back on library funding, denying teachers the basic tools of their trade. The universities are the intellectual infrastructure of the nation and, like the transport infrastructure, have been allowed to decay over the past 20 years.

A return to Newman's ideal

What is required now is a concerted effort to return the university to the Newmanian ideal, an institution whose purpose is the training of mind and character, the advancement of 'the civilizing process' and the creation of a generation of cultivated liberal gentlemen – and now ladies – who will provide informed and enlightened leadership in a world increasingly unable to distinguish between quality and trash and where the lowest common denominator demands of the market have initiated the process, expressively dubbed in America, 'the dumbing down of society'. Like the monasteries in the Dark Ages, the universities should become the beacon lights of civilized values and intellectual enquiry, undimmed by temporary ideological fads and fancies. With culture and society daily becoming, before our very eyes, more brutalized, coarsened and degraded, the need is pressing and urgent.

The furthest fall of all

the status of the clergy

Roger Homan

The loss of learning

It is a remarkable fact that the great cathedrals of Europe were designed not by professional architects but by priests. Designing and supervising the construction of major religious buildings was so much part of the job that the names of most of them have passed into oblivion, while modern architects are pleased to be held responsible for significantly lesser works. Advanced learning was then the prerogative of the clergy. Specialism is a relatively modern phenomenon.

That notion of clergy as a body of scholars in all disciplines and pursuits, of philosophers, poets and what have you, was what Coleridge imagined in his notion of the clerisy. As Weber has pointed out,[1] priestly authority in the Christian tradition has been associated with the administration of the sacraments; and in the medieval period it was exercised in conjunction with economic power.

The clergy of the Middle Ages were economically and educationally differentiated and hierarchically ordered. They ranged from the poor and barely literate parochial clergy up to a small number of bishops who were preoccupied with the high offices of state with which they were charged. Whatever their level, clergy had in common an immunity from civil law: they were constrained in all aspects of their behaviour by ecclesiastical authority and an accountability to religious superiors.

Loss of immunity

The sense of these immunities has not altogether disappeared. The claims to be judged not by secular principles and procedures and to be spared the critical view of the laity survive among some types at the end of the twentieth century. However, the effect of the Reformation was to subject the clergy to civil procedures and to dissolve the religious houses which supplied the parish churches. The system of 'livings' by which rectors and vicars secured their financial support and from which they paid – seldom generously – the parochial clergy, persisted. It afforded time for literary and other pursuits, such as those of the poet Hawker of Morwenstowe and the natural historian of Selborne, Gilbert White. It also supported a leisured class of clergy who were more observable in respectable society than at the altar or in the pulpit. Jane Austen invites us to assess her clergymen not by their spirituality or learning but by their eligibility. But then Jane Austen is only part of the story: she observes the workplace as rarely as we glimpse it in modern Australian soaps. Even as she wrote, there was a call to more serious service for the clergy and in the year after her death, the Church Building Act invested in the Lords Commissioner one million pounds to provide for every person in the land a pew within hearing of a pulpit. The building of commodious Commissioners' churches or 'preaching boxes' in the Established church peaked in the 1870s. The clergy of the towns were exercised in a way that those of the countryside were not. Preaching, being a performance, is appreciated and its practitioners are followed not by virtue of power or learning but for communication and rapport. The notions of skills and persona had entered the reckoning. The tension between what a man is and what a man does – which since 1992 has also applied to a woman – is a critical issue in the self-definition of clergy as professionals.

In response to accelerated social change in the nineteenth century, the Church of England resumed some of the social and educational functions it had lost at the Reformation. The urban churches of the Oxford Movement were particularly active in offering education and relief to the poor. But by degrees the state relieved the Established church of many of these functions. The dispensation of relief to the poor and the administration of health are now formally the responsibilities of the state. So too education, in being made compulsory, has been removed from the voluntary providers.

Loss of clientele

Inevitably the morale of a profession relates to the extent and commitment of its clientele. In the Church of England clergy can derive little comfort from the statistics or experience of membership and attendance. According to Peter Brierley, membership of the mainstream churches fell by 10 per cent in the period 1975 to 1990.[2] Membership of the Anglican churches in the United Kingdom has declined from 2.3 million in 1975 to 1.9 million in 1990 and is projected to fall still further to 1.4 million in 2010. The British phenomenon has been typified by Grace Davie as 'believing without belonging'.[3] It is the opposite of a country like Sweden in which church attendance is low but commitment by affiliation and financial support is high and the Church is the acknowledged provider of certain kinds of care and counsel.

So the learning which once distinguished the clerical profession has been divided and distributed. The power which it formerly yielded has been usurped. The immunity which its members once enjoyed has been withdrawn. And the clientele which it once served has now diminished.

The rise of the laity

In the twentieth century the spread of education, the rise of a middle class and the decline in vocations to the church's ministry have been factors in the greater participation of the laity in church affairs, including worship. At the beginning of the nineteenth century, the universities of Oxford and Cambridge were exclusive institutions of the Church of England and their function was largely to produce clergy. Chadwick records that the Oxford crew of eight which rowed in the first Henley boat race in 1829 became one bishop, two deans, one prebendary and four other clergymen.[4] Oxbridge education was clearly the sufficient foundation of a career in the Church.

This orientation was compromised when, in 1834, against the advice to the House of Lords of the Duke of Wellington, university education was extended to dissenters. In the twentieth century, the Church of England recruits from a wider range of educational backgrounds, although the great majority of its bishops still come from public schools and Oxbridge.[5]

The separate provision of theological colleges relates to a particular understanding of vocation that is not implied in higher education. Selection is as much on the basis of character and intention as upon academic background. The clerical profession of the late twentieth century is more heterogeneous both in its recruitment and in the engagement of its members.

To the extent that Oxford and Cambridge dons were formerly required to be ordained in the Church of England but derived their financial support from the colleges in which they taught, there has long been a non-stipendiary ministry. But that for which one third of Anglican ordinands are now destined is rather different. Non-stipendiary ministers work weekdays in all walks of life and undertake the work of priest in a part-time capacity.

The sharing of tasks with the laity

Again, in 1995 one in three of those ordained five years earlier were working outside the parish context, most commonly in chaplaincy or in an advisory role. One in three prepared for ordination not in a college but on a part-time, non-residential course. Further, since 1992 the Church of England has admitted women to its ministry.

The notion of the clerical gathering or 'chapter' is thus transformed: it is no longer an homogeneous group with relatively common perceptions of role and status, but a meeting of ordained butchers, bakers, candlestick-makers and women, some of whom send their apologies because they cannot get away from work. It may also include licensed lay workers and others who are not ordained. The boundaries of the profession and the laity are thus becoming blurred.

Equally, the activities which in the Anglican and Roman Catholic churches have been traditionally assigned to the clergy are now more widely shared. There are lay catechists and the administration of the chalice is, in Roman Catholic and Anglican churches, undertaken by lay persons after appropriate preparation. The home-grown is validated not only in the widespread use being made of house-groups but in the leading of worship by those with talents in music. Synodical government has enfranchised the laity at national, diocesan and local levels. Brierley reckons that 'those churches which put an emphasis on participation and experience seem to grow'.[6]

Zones of professional engagement: sanctuary and the diminishing sacred isolation of the priest

Sanctuary is a place or space of removal from a profane world. It is the mountain top above the cloud where Moses met the Lord and received the Ten Commandments. In Orthodox churches it is the area behind the *ikonastasis* where the priest goes alone. It is the altar table of Catholic and Anglican usage. It is the act of prayer. Those who dwell in the sanctuary are untouchable. It is not a zone of intersection between priest and people. Intentions for which prayers are offered are not up for discussion. One of the functions of vestments is to disguise the person and present the role. The faithful can no more enter into dialogue with a vestal priest than can double-glazing salesmen approach the guards on duty outside Buckingham Palace: we must wait until they are out of uniform and out of role.

In recent years this detachment from the human domain of the faithful has in various ways been compromised. People have started to set some store by whether churches are warm and friendly places. The priest does not turn his back on the congregation. Rather than face God together, the priest and people face each other across the altar table. They exchange a sacred greeting 'Peace be with you' which in some places lapses into a secular greeting like 'are you feeling better?'. That this is perceived as a celebration of relationships which develop outside the eucharist is apparent when individuals seek out friends elsewhere in the congregation: they operate a kind of Peace list rather like a Christmas card list. At the altar rail, in some places, the minister addresses communicants by name: 'Charlie, the Blood of Christ'. The script of the sanctuary has been rewritten and the human dimension has been introduced.

The reverse is also observable. A skilled practitioner can at a moment's notice construct sanctuary and take refuge within it. He or she may give a theological assurance, refer issues to prayer, claim the assent of the Holy Spirit, appeal to values like love and the building of the Kingdom. The effect if not the intention of this pattern of behaviour, of which examples are given below, is to define judgements or intentions as non-negotiable. It is a defence mechanism, the very deployment of which tells us something about the perceptions of the clergy toward the laity who may have been admitted too far for comfort to the domains in which they and their deliberations have traditionally been inaccessible.

The pulpit: the diminution of authority

It is sometimes said that a preacher is four feet above criticism. In fact it is more complicated than that. The pulpits of the Counter-Reformation in the great churches of Ghent, for example, are rather higher, while the reordering of churches since Vatican II has involved the removal of pulpits and the bringing down of preachers to ground level.

Being above criticism, however, is not merely a matter of altitude: it is a matter of style. Chaucer's Pardoner knew the reality of a legitimation crisis and had strategies to pre-empt it:

Oure lige lordes seel on my patente,
That shewe I first my body to warrente,
That no man be so boold, ne preest ne clerk,
Me to distourbe of Cristes hooly werk.

He quoted in Latin his text *Radix malorum est cupiditas* so that his hearers would not recognize that he was preaching against his own worst vice of avarice. This indeed is conspiracy and of such practice Shaw's famous remark is fair comment.

The Second Vatican Council, whose impact is felt far beyond the Roman church, outlawed the mystification of the laity. Nothing was to be uttered that was not understood by the simplest soul present. The Bible is read in modern language and is thought thereby to be more accessible. And the sermon is reduced to a few simple, soothing words uttered at ground level and addressed to 'my dear friends'. The applications of the Word are commonly explored in house-groups and in some places there is space after the reading of the Gospel for any of those present to contribute their own insights. The basis of authority is neither learning nor vocation but everyday experience.

Vestry: the simulation of sanctuary

Some time ago the author of this chapter was a member of a parochial church council representing a middle-brow congregation in the middle range of churchmanship. It cherished its Evensong but for its principal worship looked to the eucharist. The vicar thought it would be a good idea if parochial church council meetings were to be held in the context of the eucharist. The council, it was suggested, should precede its meetings with Holy Communion and so define its business as an endeavour to build the kingdom of God. The proposal was unassailable and no-one opposed it at the time.

Indeed, even when introduced and some unease was experienced, none of us quite knew how to banish from our meetings something as sacred as the eucharist. Members arrived at the vestry where silence prevailed. The vicar would sit at one end of the table: if he was not at prayer, it was at least evident that he was not in a position to be disturbed and the usual greetings of 'hello' and 'good evening' were not given as people arrived. The vicar had the chalice in front of him and the booklets giving the order of service were set out at each place. He wore a suit, stock, dog-collar and stole. After communion but before the blessing, agenda papers were brought out and the meetings started as usual with apologies. The vicar's voice was hushed from the outset and, following his example, we found ourselves almost whispering. If a voice was raised or his opinion on any matter disputed with any force, he would touch the service book still open in front of him and remind us 'we've not yet had the blessing'.

In retrospect, one sees this to have been an extraordinary procedure. The dynamics of the altar had been conveyed into the committee room with the effect, if not the intention, of securing a kind of immunity for the priest in the chair. But one can see what had led to this. When, in commending a particular weekly offering scheme, he had said 'there are very good theological reasons but we cannot go into them here', he may well have noticed that there were on the council three theology graduates, one from Durham, one from Newcastle and one from King's London. He who was trained in history could not, in the 1980s, appeal to theology and hope the assurance would go uncontested.

When theology or worldly wisdom cease to be the prerogative of the clergy, it is necessary to introduce some other basis of immunity.

'Coffee': the passing of authority

The human population of parishes grows while the attendances of their churches decline. As the proportion of one to the other has increased and as the number of clergy serving parishes has declined, the habit of visiting has widely lapsed. The cure of souls is relatively seldom exercised by knocking on doors. Clergy time is not much occupied with speculative visiting: in some parishes visiting is delegated to the laity. The consequence is that they are not as closely acquainted with all sorts and conditions of men as were their forbears, nor as practised in being polite about parishioners' home-made cake.

The dislocation of the pastoral role is, of course, neither universal nor absolute: but it is a significant trend. It has been supplanted in two ways. First, it has been collectivized in the form of 'coffee in the hall after the service'. This affords a brief salutation with the faithful: it precludes deep spiritual counsel and it excludes those who do not come to church. Secondly, the needs and intentions of all and sundry are sanctified: they may be written on slips of paper and left in church like petitions in the Wailing Wall. It is the sacred way of dealing with needs and cares but does not necessitate face-to-face engagement between clergy and the souls in their cure. A significant aspect of this trend is that the initiative for contact between church and people has passed from the clergy.

The mystery of ordination: vocation to a state or learning skills?

An investigation among those recently ordained in the Church of England revealed aspects of a tendency to remove the nature of ministry from the domain of secular skills and to elude appraisal. The intention of the enquiry reported in *To the Altar of God*[1] was to assess the effectiveness of theological college and non-residential courses in preparing ordinands for the conduct of worship. All 357 clergy who had been ordained during 1990 in the Anglican provinces of Canterbury and York received a postal questionnaire asking about experience of different forms of worship and about their confidence to conduct them. Responses were received from 238 of those circulated, some 67 per cent. There was an articulate resistance among some clergy to the very notion that worship could be conducted competently or otherwise, to the suggestion that the conduct of worship was in any sense a skill, to the use of the word 'training' as a description of courses leading to ordination. In the subsequent interview stage of the enquiry, a smaller sample of clergy was invited to respond to a variety of descriptions of their pre-ordination programmes, each of which had featured in responses to the questionnaire: these were *training, theology, formation, learning, preparation* and *education*.

There emerged evidence of two tendencies among recently ordained clergy which we may here call the *mystical* and the *pragmatic*. In common with inspections and evaluations in the secular world of education, the questionnaire had assumed that the effectiveness of courses could be assessed in terms of the competence levels of their graduates. The mystical orientation showed up in a resistance to the competence model and prevailed among respondents from the more Catholic of the Church of England's theological colleges. The investigator's interest in the training of skills was dismissed as an irrelevance and he was more than once told that he was missing the point.

In a long letter explaining why it was not possible to answer the questionnaire, one of the clergy advised:

> The ordained life is capable up to a point of consideration as a profession, but sociological – or any other analysis – eventually breaks down because at the end of the day it is a calling to a state of being. I *am* a priest, it is not my job.
>
> Secondly, a theological college is not just about *training*. It is

one formalised element in the beginning of a diaconal and priestly formation.

Again, one of those interviewed responded to the information that one of the colleges was employing a professional actress to help with voice production:

> But anybody can have a trained voice. A layperson can have a trained voice. The point is that I am a priest.

If that view was typical of those trained at Mirfield, the antithesis was expressed by respondents from Oakhill and St John's Nottingham:

> I'd have to dump *formation*. That's catholic, almost monastic.

> I'd see that as more a High Church word.

The notion of priesthood as a matter of being rather than of doing prompted one of the interviewees to write a letter declaiming it as

> … lamentable and indefensible. Learning worship is more like an Art than a Science. You need to be taught certain skills and disciplines, of course, but beyond that you can only improve by hard work and by reflecting on a range of other human examples.

Conclusion

Those who offer themselves for the Church's ministry in these days must do so on the basis of diminished expectations. Oxbridge education is today neither sufficient nor required. Preparation is by training, by narrowing, rather than by education, by broadening. In the process of narrowing, the theological colleges play a crucial role. They are the gatekeepers of the clerical profession and they exercise an evident control over what capacities ordinands will take to their first parishes. A former student, now working in a parish, commented on his college course:

> There is a great deal of use of the Prayer Book (for offices and for 8.00am Holy Communion) and of Rite B in the Diocese which was my sponsoring Diocese. However, it was very difficult to persuade the powers that be at [college] to give very much attention to Rite B or BCP Holy Communion and I found this a drawback during my curacy.[8]

Towler and Coxon assume that the content of theological college courses will tell us what the Church of England wants of its clergy:[9] in reality, it may only tell us what the colleges are determined to deliver. In either event, the evidence is that mature entrants to the non-stipendiary ministry prepared on non-residential courses are less inclined to be influenced by their courses than college students:

> Quite often it was clear that people on the course knew a great deal more about things than the lecturer did. On the ethics course on one occasion the lecturer was talking about artificial insemination and he had a diagram on the board and one of the students said 'oh that's not how I do it'.

Again,

> If that's what I have to do, I thought, I'll do it, just as long as I get deaconed at the end of it.

So the cognitive base of preparation for the ministry has broadened and the corresponding expertise is to be found in large measure outside the profession. Those for whom it is not a profession bring relevant expertise not shared by those for whom it is.

And for those who approach ordination as the affirmation of an exclusive identity, the job increasingly offers professional discomforts. Those things which dignified the clerical profession such as social standing, a gracious vicarage and security of tenure are fast disappearing. Parsonages are being sold and replaced by smaller residences. And the practice is now to appoint in many cases a 'priest-in-charge' for a period of five years, giving the Church at large more flexibility to dispose its human resources.

For a variety of reasons of which the principal are economic, the future prospect is of a non-stipendiary ministry in the Church of England along the lines of those ministries to be found in the Nonconformist churches. For the Church of England the change is profound: the uniformity of clergy has afforded the secret of their distinctiveness. With non-stipendiary and women priests, it is increasingly seen that these are only ordinary people doing a special job.

Education, it has been said, is too important to be left to the teachers. Since 1980, parents have had statutory representation on the governing bodies of schools; since 1986, the conduct of schools has been reviewed by annual parents' meetings; under the 1988 Act, parents are entitled to regular detailed reporting of the progress of their children. House buyers can now do their own conveyancing. There are various medical kits available to conduct certain tests upon oneself at home. So the burgeoning sense that the laity does not need its clergy has parallels in other contemporary professions in Britain. What distinguishes the clerical profession is that the mystery in which it is rooted is ultimate: it is not available to the laity by the means of education and the experience of participation.

4

From wisdom to expertise
the lawyer in the USA

Michael M Uhlmann

Professions: high intelligence and elevated character

Once upon a time, a profession was chiefly distinguished from a trade by the academic training prerequisite to its practice, and by the practitioner's dedication to purposes beyond self-interest. The very idea of a profession was aristocratic in nature: only those of sufficient talent and intelligence could master the necessary skills, and only those of elevated character could be counted on to dedicate their art to the common good or the good of others. At the top of the heap were the so-called 'learned professions' – traditionally divinity, medicine, law, and (in some usages) the military – for which moral excellence was a constituent element of their proper practice. The tidy teleological symmetry of this grouping bore the ancient stamp of classical and Christian teaching: the learned professions were those pre-eminently associated with the perfection of man's soul, of his body, and of the relationships constituting the civil order. Our egalitarian era mocks this traditional dispensation. Universal education and the exponential growth of science, technology, and commerce have combined to ensure that the ancient distinction between learned profession and commercial trade, never altogether precise to begin with, can no longer be sustained.

Today the professional-trade distinction eroded

Nowadays, more or less everyone seems to qualify as a professional of some sort. Not long ago I happened upon a television talk-show – one of those ubiquitous chat-'em-ups that fill the airwaves – on which some utterly forgettable issue of social policy was being discussed. In addition to the host (a nattily attired, carefully coiffed time-keeper and shuffler of note cards), the participants included a brace of newshounds, an elected official, a bureaucrat or two, a social worker, and someone described in the electronic box beneath his picture as a 'Community Activist'. All of these participants – including the man whose activities, I gather, consisted more or less exclusively in political agitation – would undoubtedly consider themselves professionals. Why indeed not?

The truth in our time is that almost every economic undertaking, from ballplayer to beautician, has been elevated to the status of a profession. Just ask your barber (who is likely to be called a 'hairstylist') what he thinks about 'hair-cutters' who offer their services at a sharp discount. What has happened, of course, is that profession has come to mean little more than expertise, and expertise now refers to almost any putative skill or body of knowledge, regardless of subject matter, and regardless of the educational attainment or character of its possessor. One half expects these days to encounter a talk-show composed entirely of teenagers bearing labels like 'Suburban Mall Enthusiast' or 'High School Attendee'.

Despite this egalitarian levelling, contemporary usage nevertheless retains (in spite of itself) something of the old dispensation. It is true that the learned professions are far more numerous than they once were and that genuine expertise has multiplied in quantity and complexity beyond imagining. It is also true that scoundrels abide in every calling. But whereas a professor of chemistry, say, who happens to be a bounder neither disgraces science nor rouses distinctive public ire, special scorn is still reserved for the miscreant clergyman, doctor, lawyer, or military officer.

Good character still matters where it is supposed to matter, and the animating spirit of the ancient learned profession is still distinguished by the idea of duty to others.

Yet people still expect particularly high standards from professions such as law

There are, to be sure, quack doctors, corrupt preachers, and cowardly military officers, just as there are shyster lawyers, but lawyers have been the particular butt of popular scorn for longer than anyone can remember. Lawyer jokes, which play precisely on the difference between selfishness and service to others, trace their ancestry from the ancient world. They were alive and well in the works of Shakespeare, and 250 years after his death, Charles Dickens could safely portray the legal profession as so much organized chicanery. His acidic *Bleak*

House caricature, for all its exaggeration, continues to resonate with readers far removed from the stultifying atmosphere of nineteenth-century English chancery courts. Whatever one may think of such sentiments on an objective view, there is nothing quite like them to be found in discussions of other learned professions. What accounts for this dubious distinction is not so easy to discern. Every profession, as I say, has its scoundrels. Perhaps it is the number of legal practitioners, or the very nature of the legal undertaking itself, where clever argument and procedural pettifoggery sometimes triumph at the expense of truth and substance. Perhaps it is the particular passion men attach to questions of justice (seldom more so than in their own cause) when justice fails, as it sometimes does, blaming lawyers may be but the expression of our disappointment in the consequences of fallen nature.

Whatever the cause of long-standing popular disdain for lawyering, there is another part to the story, one that at times acquires the aspect of heroic mythology. Even when justice falls short, men continue to celebrate the rule of law as the expression of their noblest ambitions and, no less, of the nobility of the legal profession itself. This understanding finds its roots in both biblical and classical teaching, where the rule of law is seen as the mediating instrument, *par excellence*, between civilization and barbarity, between divine ordinance and the capacity of men to order their lives in accordance with justice. In this respect, a lawyer's activity, even when it focuses on relations among private parties, is inextricably intertwined with the good order of the political community. The dignity of the legal profession, Burke said, arises from its association 'with the highest temporal interests of man – property, reputation, the peace of families, the arbitration and peace of nations, liberty, life even, and the very foundations of society'.

Lawyers once America's aristocracy, the anchor of social stability

This elevated view of lawyering provides a necessary counterweight to the jaundiced view of Dickens. And nowhere has Burke's sentiment been taken more seriously than in the American Republic – the first regime in history founded explicitly on the proposition that the rule of law should be the norm, not the exception, in the conduct of human affairs. It was no accident that the founding documents of the American regime were for the most part the work of men trained in the law. The defining instrument of the new nation, the Declaration of Independence, was in effect a brief filed in the court of enlightened opinion that appealed for its authority to the laws of nature and nature's God, not only to justify its separation from the mother country but to establish a moral foundation for the legitimacy of the Constitution that would later follow. Early American legal practitioners, invoking what Lincoln would later call 'the mystic cordes of memory', took pains to connect the activities of their profession to the noble events of the nation's founding. To peruse almost any of the early nineteenth-century law reports, even on mundane subjects, is to be astounded by the gravity of purpose, eloquence, and public-spiritedness of advocates and judges alike.

On his visit to the United States in the 1830s, Alexis de Tocqueville was much taken with this phenomenon. He famously remarked of lawyers in American society that they constituted the closest thing to an aristocracy he had observed in the fledgling nation. What he had in mind was not a propertied or titled class, on the European model, to counterbalance the egalitarian envy of the lower classes, but a distinguished group of citizens who would uphold the rule of law against the self-interested claims of the *demos* and would-be oligarchs alike. Lawyers, he believed, would become the anchor of social and political stability precisely by virtue of their attachment to the principles of a permanent constitutional order of which they were the chief custodians.

One can, of course, exaggerate the nobility of early American lawyers. And, without question, those who came to prominence in the decades after the founding period were decidedly more mundane in their interests. The unprecedented rise in commercial activity, the geographical dispersal of legal and political authority, and the widespread availability of cheap land created an enormous demand for attorneys throughout the country. Whereas the founders' generation received their legal training at the Inns of Court or at one of the fledgling American universities that taught law as part of the liberal arts, the new breed of commercial lawyer who later flourished received little in the way of formal training. Admission to legal practice was not difficult in many areas, and in a few states one didn't even have to be an attorney to represent clients in court. The legal profession very quickly became a middle-class franchise, a vehicle for upward social mobility and political ambition. It created abundant opportunity as well for reprobates, fast-buck artists, and legal snake-oil salesmen of every stripe. Nevertheless, even these found it necessary to cloak their self-promotion in the forms of social and legal propriety. They would not have dared to defend their behaviour in public, nor would mere cunning have been celebrated in the popular media of the day. The dignity of the rule of law American-style, however poorly understood or followed in practice, was capable of taming the baser motives of all but the most cynical practitioners. The idea of law as a public calling, in short, retained a certain irreducible vitality even in the hurly-burly of an expanding commercial empire.

Law regarded as a particular calling as late as the mid-twentieth century

That same vitality was still apparent, albeit in diminished form, in the education of those who attended law school as late as a generation ago. From opening lecture to graduating ceremony, legal education, for all its attention to the acquisition of marketable commercial skills, conveyed the unmistakable sense that law was in some significant way a calling. Although everyone took for granted that one could make a comfortable living at the bar, making money was understood to be incidental to the loftier goals of the profession – and to the pride one took in mastering a craft so intimately concerned with the public good.

A friend of mine, now a distinguished judge, recalls an address to his first-year class by the Dean of the Harvard Law School in 1958. They were bluntly informed that if wealth was their goal, they should straightaway trot across campus to the business school and get on with it. 'Practising law itself,' my friend remarks, 'was regarded as *pro bono*'.

Public service yields to money making and skill for its own sake

Adherents of this belief may still be found, but the tradition that nurtured the sentiment is no longer honoured as it once was, either in the schools or at the bar. That, at least, is the proposition advanced by two thoughtful observers who are in a position to know what they are talking about. In a work published in 1994 and entitled, appropriately enough, *The Lost Lawyer*, Dean Anthony Kronman of the Yale Law School argues that the legal profession in America is in serious trouble and unlikely to get better anytime soon. When practitioners aren't devoting themselves to getting and spending, he says, they are almost obsessively preoccupied with the mastery of technique for its own sake. That is to say, they pride themselves on having acquired a powerful set of skills but see little purpose in their professional lives other than to deploy those skills, ruthlessly if need be, on behalf of their clients or their own personal agendas.

Dean Kronman traces the rise of this sentiment to the intellectual fashions of contemporary legal education, particularly the Critical Legal Studies and the Law and Economics movements, which reduce legal knowledge to a subset of a more architectonic understanding – in the first case to the interests of gender, race, or class that are said to constitute the true essence of law; and in the latter, to the motivations of *homo economicus*. This new emphasis, Kronman says, necessarily belittles, ignores, or denies the importance of character and practical wisdom in the practice of law. Whereas earlier generations of American lawyers 'conceived their highest goal to be the attainment of a wisdom that lies beyond technique', the contemporary lawyer tends to seek fulfilment in the external benefits of his labour – money or social status, for example – rather than in the mastery of a public-spirited calling. The rule of law, so long celebrated as the distinctive dividing line between civilization and barbarity, is now commonly understood in the law schools as little but the public expression of dominant interests, be they psychological, racial, social, or economic. Justice, in this view, reduces itself to the interest of the stronger – precisely the proposition against which the rule of law was erected in the first place.

Law's lost duty to community – replaced by duty to client

Dean Kronman's opinion is echoed in many respects by Mary Ann Glendon, the Learned Hand Professor of Law at Harvard. In her 1993 book, *A Nation Under Lawyers*, Professor Glendon laments the disappearance of pride in legal craft and its replacement by a kind of cynical gamesmanship that values winning at almost any cost. The adulation of power, fame, and riches, so often the theme of media depictions of lawyers, seems to have taken hold of the profession itself. Like Kronman, Glendon decries the severance of legal practice, especially in large commercial firms, from obligations to the political community and from any sense of justice beyond self-interest or that of clients. This new attitude, Glendon argues, is the inevitable consequence of the positivism and relativism that for a generation or more have rooted themselves in the leading law schools.

If one wishes to understand how modern practitioners see themselves, the place to start is with the portrayal of law in the curricula of these schools. Little will be found there to provide an ennobling sense of the law, or of the attorney's role in sustaining it. One discovers instead a variety of post-modern shibboleths that have as their common premise the assertion that truth has no objective grounding. The modern law curriculum, Glendon says, rests on a series of assumptions that have acquired the character of holy writ among the intelligentsia – for example,

> that we live under a rule of men, not law; that the Constitution is just an old text that means whatever the current crop of judges say it does; that all rules (including the rules of professional ethics) are infinitely manipulable; that law is a business like any other; and that business is just the unrestrained pursuit of self-interest.

The power of such assumptions rests less on their logic – they are seldom seriously debated in the law schools – than on the fact that so many among the professoriate gratuitously hold them as true. A generation of attorneys trained to believe such things, it goes without saying, will find little room for the idea of law as a public calling.

The arguments advanced by Dean Kronman and Professor Glendon are dismissed by some as rarefied, professorial opinion that prescinds from the 'real' world of legal practice. The trouble is not only that Kronman and Glendon are very familiar indeed with the mores of contemporary lawyering, but that their views have been confirmed, if somewhat less elegantly, by leading practitioners themselves. One can hardly visit a bookstore these days without encountering some new lament about the profession written by senior lawyers or disaffected junior associates, who chronicle the decline of professional standards, the dominion of self-interest and the billable hour, and the fixation with financial growth and profits.

The legal press, which is obsessed with the clinical detail of law-as-business, is filled these days with profiles of prominent attorneys and their firms, discussions of marketing strategies, detailed analyses of law firm costs and revenues, billable hours and rates for partners and associates, comparisons of everything from starting salaries for new lawyers to per-partner profits, and endless rumour and gossip, some of which may even have the advantage of being true. What you will seldom find in these precincts is any coherent discussion of whether and how the legal profession differs in kind from any other business. One would be equally hard-pressed to encounter such a discussion in our major centres of legal learning, or in the corridors of leading law firms. Yes, attorneys have always been torn between the necessities of commerce and the higher calling of their profession. The conflict today, however, is both quantitatively larger and qualitatively different from any that has arisen before. The suspicion is widespread, among lawyer and non-lawyer alike, that Dean Kronman may be right when he says that the profession 'now stands in danger of losing its soul'.

Law without its soul

The good news – if you happen to be a lawyer – is that the legal recession of the late 1980s and early 1990s appears to have abated. During the downturn, which followed nearly a quarter-century of unprecedented growth, firms found it necessary to trim their sails. Firm shrinkage, office consolidation, and declining profits became the order of the day. Firms that had, like Topsy, 'jus' growed' during 1970s and early 1980s were forced to take a hard look at what they had become. And what most of them discovered, willy-nilly, is that they had become a business, one in which almost all distinctions between trade and profession were relegated to ceremonial occasions. The second thing they seem to have discovered is that the first discovery didn't bother them very much at all. Cost curves, revenue projections, marketing strategies, and other financial tools characteristic of the business firm had entered the everyday argot of law-firm management.

A managing partner of a large law firm these days is frequently less well-known or less valued for his legal skill than for his business acumen. He spends most of his time worrying about the same things that preoccupy manufacturers of goods or sellers of non-professional services: how to reduce costs, raise profits, and increase output and market share. The practice of law, to be sure, has never been indifferent to the same economic necessities that confront the rest of the race, but during the past 25 or 30 years it has become harder and harder to distinguish what many law firms do from any other line of economic activity.

The dominance of large corporate law firms

Here it is necessary to add a few facts about the size and structure of the American bar. There are approximately 900,000 lawyers in the United States, about three quarters of whom are actively engaged in practice. Among these, approximately a third are solo practitioners. Of the rest, 27 per cent are employed by government, corporations, or universities, or engaged in non-law-related work; 13 per cent will be found in firms of two to five lawyers, and another 11 per cent in firms of six to 19 lawyers. Of the 16 per cent who practice in groups of 20 or more lawyers, only a small fraction is affiliated with very large firms, ie, those with 100 or more attorneys. Whereas solo or small-firm practitioners are primarily concerned with the representation of individuals or small businesses (eg, real estate, family law, smaller tax and commercial transactions, petty crime), the business of large firms is dominated by the needs of large corporations, either in their private undertakings or (increasingly) in the effort to direct or deflect governmental regulatory activity. Significantly, very little attention is paid to the activities of smaller firms, despite their number, in comparison to the mores of the larger firms, which have furnished forth the plots of numerous novels and films. Ambitious law students dream of fabulous incomes and corner offices in towering skyscrapers, all the while advising the captains of industry and government officials on matters of great social and economic import. Whether or not this preoccupation with the business of large corporate firms is justifiable, the fact is that, for good or ill, they tend to set the tone for the profession as a whole. That is why the changes that have occurred among them during the past generation deserve particular attention.

Those changes could not be more dramatic. Indeed, a suddenly revenant senior partner from a major 1960s firm would hardly recognize his old haunts today. Size alone tells much of the tale. The number of attorneys has more than tripled in the past 35 years (there is now one lawyer for every 280 Americans), but even more striking is what has happened to the size and distribution of firms. Whereas the largest firm in the nation in 1960 housed 125 lawyers, that size today wouldn't make the top 250 list. There are now 352 firms with 50-100 lawyers; 275 with 100-300; 73 with 300-99, and even three firms with more than 1,000 lawyers.

Total paid legal services US$122 billion of which US$16 billion for top 100 firms

Total paid legal services in the United States in 1995 amounted to some $122 billion, $16 billion of which was accounted for by the top 100 firms alone. Starting salaries for junior associates in the large firms have increased by 1,000 per cent or more since 1960. Bright, freshly minted law school graduates can expect to earn $70-90,000 in their first year of practice with large firms in major commercial cities. Seventh-year associates (those a year or two away from partnership, who are the most valuable producers on the legal reservation) can go as high as $200,000 annually in salary, often much higher when bonuses are taken into account. The typical baseline for a partner's salary in one of the largest 250 firms would be somewhere around a quarter of a million dollars, rising with age, skill, and location to three or four times that amount. The practice of law in a big firm, whose revenues typically run well into hundreds of millions of dollars, has become a very big business indeed.

But none of these gross statistical measures, striking as they are, give the full measure of the qualitative change that has come over the practice of law in the past generation. Not so very long ago, the large corporate firms were predominantly (some would say insufferably) 'white shoe', peopled as they were by the genteel sons of the WASP establishment. Women, Catholics, Jews, racial minorities, and graduates of non-prestige schools were rarely, if ever, found in their midst. Client relationships were long-standing and stable, and it was common for a corporation to rely upon a single outside firm for all its legal needs. A partner in charge of a client's affairs would frequently sit on the client's board of directors, and few corporations had in-house legal staffs of any size. Billable hours, to the extent they were used at all, were at most a loose and casually monitored index of performance. Most work was undertaken on a retainer or fixed-fee basis, subject to revision from time to time in the event of unforeseen or unusually laborious engagements. Partners tended to wed one firm (and one wife) for life; lateral moves to other firms were unheard of. Partners could expect to earn a comfortable, but not necessarily luxuriant living.

Erosion of client-firm relationship and collegiality
Almost none of these features holds true of the large corporate firm of the 1990s. Their once-dominant white-male Protestant culture is a mere shadow of its former self. Stability of firm-client relationships is likewise a thing of the past. Many corporations now employ large in-house legal staffs for problems once referred to their outside law firms. Corporate general counsel routinely shop major legal engagements among more than a few firms, and individual lawyers or speciality practice groups within firms are far more important to them than the firms as such. In turn, individual lawyers and their affiliated practice groups shift their practice from one firm to another with an ease and frequency that would have been thought scandalous a generation ago. The billable hour has come to dominate both the politics and the economics of internal firm management and its billing practices with clients. Collegiality among big-firm attorneys is at best accidental:

according to a recent survey, some 80 per cent of the partners at the largest 125 firms either infrequently or never socialize with their colleagues outside the office. Increasingly, they view their careers as a means to the acquisition of considerable wealth. And, as earlier indicated, partnership with a large corporate firm can lead to an income that, scarcely a generation ago, would have been thought beyond the dreams of avarice.

The causes – increase of regulation in employment, discrimination, environment, Medicare

The reasons for these spectacular changes are complicated, but one fact dominates all others: the demand for legal services has grown with an economy that is many times larger than it was in the 1960s. Economic growth has been accompanied by a comparable expansion of governmental activity at all levels, from town to nation. It is simply no longer possible for even a small firm to operate without entanglement with numerous layers of regulatory authority. Large fields of law simply unknown a generation ago now generate a substantial amount of legal activity – health care, environmental regulation, employment discrimination, pension law, international trade, to name only a few. The governance of Medicare, the Federal Government's old-age medical services programme, has resulted in some 50,000 pages of regulations, and government standards for pension plans alone run to two shelf-feet.

In such an atmosphere, one can hardly do without a lawyer, and as long as the growth of government keeps pace with the growth of the economy, the demand for legal services will expand apace. Indeed, the rate of growth for American lawyers in the future may even exceed the pace of the past three decades. Given the dominion of American economic interests throughout the world, we are now witnessing what might be called the 'Americanization' of private commercial law in international activities – a kind of *ius commune* whose principles are being incorporated into the case law, and even the statutory law, of other nations. Just as much of the world has come to imitate the pattern of American capitalism so it is imitating the American style of legal practice that inevitably accompanies it. This fact has not escaped the larger American law firms, who are moving aggressively into international markets, either by establishing franchises of their own or by forging strategic alliances with foreign law firms wishing to pattern themselves on the American model.

More professional erosion ahead

In short, there is every indication that the internal growth of the American legal market will continue, perhaps even accelerate, in the years ahead, and that the momentum will proceed apace into international markets. This will undoubtedly enhance the personal financial portfolios of those engaged in the trade, but is unlikely to remind them why practising law is different from selling soap. In some respects, of course, it isn't: there is nothing particularly uplifting or public-spirited about most of the regulatory filings, procedural motions, or commercial negotiations routinely undertaken by lawyers every day. And if that is all lawyers do, or wish to do, then perhaps the idea of law as a calling has simply outlived its day. Still, those old enough to recall an earlier era know what has been lost. A lawyer who confines himself to the commercial aspects of lawyering and steers clear of *res publica* 'makes sad work with his biography'. So said Horace Binney, a prominent figure of the nineteenth-century bar. He continued:

> You might almost as well undertake to write the biography of a mill-horse. It is at best a succession of concentric circles, widening a little perhaps from year to year, but never, when most enlarged, getting away from the centre. He always has before him the same things, the same places, the same men, and the same end ... The more a man is a lawyer, the less he has to say of himself ... The biography of lawyers, however eminent *qua* lawyers, is nothing.

5

The lawyer as hired gun

the case of Europe

Fernand Keuleneer

Lawyers doing so many different tasks – are they still a profession?

In continental Europe, as elsewhere, lawyers are active in many different sectors of society. They are, of course, actors in the judicial system, as judges, public prosecutors or advocates. Some have found their place in the civil service. For some 20-25 years now, law firms have been growing and focusing upon counselling corporate clients outside any litigation context. Businesses themselves hire an increasing number of in-house lawyers. These developments raise a number of questions. To what extent do lawyers in Europe still form a 'profession'? And do their respective and different practices still share a common nature? If so, is that common nature still the practice of something called 'law'?

To address these issues, I propose to focus upon the lawyers in private practice, ie, those who are sole practitioners or partners of, or otherwise working for, a 'law firm'. Not only because that is the area which I know perhaps something about on the basis of personal experience, but also because I believe that major changes have occurred and are occurring in that area.

The profession as it was

Continental Europe, with the exception of the Netherlands, does not have a tradition of law firms. Practising attorneys were most often sole practitioners, with a few *stagiaires* (interns) and perhaps a couple of associates. They counselled clients when they had a 'legal problem', sometimes an important contract which had to be entered into, most often a dispute to be settled or litigated. Typically, they were generalists, able to assist clients in whatever problem of a legal nature. The link with the court system was symbolized by the group name of the profession: 'the Bar'. Bar councils supervised the members of the Bar and regulated the profession. The contents of that regulation tell us something about the nature of the profession as it was perceived in the old days. Very often, communications between members of the Bar on a particular case were considered to be confidential, ie, they could not be disclosed to one's own client. Lawyers were not allowed to visit clients at the latter's address; meetings had to take place in the lawyer's office. Advertising was not allowed. Fees were freely determined, taking into account various factors such as the amount of time spent on a case, the result obtained, the importance of the case, and the situation of the client. Disputes about fees were submitted to the Bar council.

The charge against the old profession – corporatist and protectionist

It is not surprising that not all, but a good deal of this has changed or is changing. What is surprising, however, is that a young, ambitious lawyer entering the practice now doesn't have a clue as to why these conventions and regulations existed. They are thought of as 'corporatism', 'caste protection' or 'violation of the free market'. Some of this may be true, but these comments show one of two things: either young lawyers do not understand at all how the legal profession was seen and saw itself, or they do understand, but their concept of legal practice is a totally different one. What is striking is the virtually complete lack of ordered argument as to why the legal profession should not be organized as it used to be. Usually one doesn't get any further than: 'Law is a business like any other business' or 'I should be able to do whatever I want to do', or 'This is just a clique protecting their own position in society'. This kind of 'argument' can come from the right or from the left, but it usually boils down to the refusal to accept any imposed restrictions on its own impulses or *modi operandi*. Is this the right way to think about a profession? Or does it mean that a profession no longer exists?

The double loyalty of lawyer to the client and to law itself

Let's take a step back. Lawyers have always had, at least, a double loyalty: on the one hand to their client, on the other hand to the law. The lawyer was never supposed to be a blind advocate or a hired gun for his clients. It is the role of a lawyer to defend the interests of his client while upholding the letter and the spirit of the law. Now, this mission presupposes a number of things: that the lawyer is someone with the highest moral and professional standards, honestly and in a talented way trying to achieve this mission; and that there exists something like a coherent body of legal rules and principles, called the law. To the extent that one or the other is lacking, the system does not work and power takes over from the law as the mechanism to settle disputes. A lawyer who looks upon the law exclusively as an instrument to enhance his client's interests, without consideration for civilized public order, part of which is the law, has more characteristics of a predator than of a lawyer. Such a type of lawyer, using the law as a weapon, is perhaps not as different as he would like to think from a gang member using a gun. A society destroying a coherent public order, or tolerating its destruction, invites this type of lawyering.

The rise of law firms

Whether lawyers are sole practitioners or practice within the context of a larger firm, should not, in theory at least, influence their duties as a lawyer. However, we cannot and should not avoid the question of what kind of influence, if any, the relatively recent rise of law firms on the continent has had. The advantages which law firms have claimed to offer have differed and evolved over time. Originally, and still to a large extent, the emphasis was on economies of scale, ie, the ability to offer top-notch specialized advice in all areas of the law. In this view, the client would have a long-term relationship with the law firm, which could, as a one-stop shop, offer all the legal services the client needed. The billing would be based on the number of billable hours worked on a project. The hourly rates of top partners were high, decreasing along the lines of seniority to associate rates.

The firm was thought of as an entity. It was realized that some partners were specialists in their substantive area, giving excellent advice, while others were particularly good at client getting ('rain-making'). This division of labour was accepted and did not lead to differences in share or compensation, which were almost exclusively based upon seniority (the 'lockstep system'). Bringing clients to the firm was not a pre-condition for partnership. Associates with the right professional qualities would become partners. The collective result of the firm was considered to be the fruit of a collective effort. The firm was a true and unique entity; switching among firms was simply not done.

Few would recognize in the description above a true and fair view of the practice today, or if it still is, of what they expect the practice tomorrow to look like. Somehow, the nature of the firm seems to have changed, and this change does not seem to have had a positive impact upon the practice of law, or even upon the law as such.

The change in law firms' identity

What are the symptoms and signs of a changing law firm? Let's start at the bottom of the ladder. Unlike his predecessors, a *stagiaire* or associate entering a firm is rarely exposed these days to the full scope and flavour of legal practice. Straight after law school, he (or increasingly she) is immediately assigned to one of the firm's 'departments' where he will become a 'specialist' in a very small or fairly small area of the law (or the regulatory system which today is called law). This means that he enters an organization which is less interested in recruiting good (potential) lawyers, than in finding people who make the wheels of the machine turn around faster. If such is the case, however, the stage is set. For the young lawyer, it becomes clear after a short while that he has entered an organization which is primarily interested in his immediate short-term contribution to the firm's annual results. Furthermore, it becomes clear as well that the only way to compete with fellow associates for the scarce partnership positions is to contribute more than one's competitors, which associates do by working longer hours (or, more accurately, billing more hours).

Let us now take the view from the top, where, of course, the origin of the above development must be sought. What factors can turn a law firm into a money-making machine? First of all, there are factors such as the heavy cost-structure of a large firm. In more difficult economic circumstances, firms look for higher, speedier and easier revenue. Secondly, lawyers generally are not very good managers of their own affairs. So they hire expert management consultants to tell them how they should run their firms. Invariably, one will then get the usual prescriptions so dear to the caste of consultants: re-engineer the firm up from profit centres, cut costs to a minimum, give people incentives to work harder. Summarized: individualize the firm, make sure that no-one gets out more than he puts in and do this on the basis we have in common – billing.

Whether this is good firm management is a question which I do not intend to address here. One effect is certain, however: in the process, the focus has shifted from the practice of law as a partnership to the structuring of the firm like any other business. Combine this with the third factor and you get an explosive cocktail. This third factor is a cultural-moral one. How do lawyers see themselves and perceive their own role? If greed and the unrestricted drive to maximise revenue become the driving forces (and why should they not in the present cultural and moral climate?) it is hardly surprising that the structure of a law firm would suffer the consequences.

Greed and profit – a business like any other

Now, what could there be wrong with the profit motive in the practice of law? There is no doubt that to some extent all professional activity is a form of business, that a business must have higher revenue than costs in order to survive, and that those involved in the business must have a decent income and will naturally strive for more. This is all good and normal. But does that make a law firm into a firm like any other?

I mentioned the double loyalty which a lawyer has to honour. Does that double duty constitute perhaps the difference with other businesses? Yes and no. The answer is definitely 'no' if a 'yes' were to imply that other businesses have no moral duty to their customers. I am most definitely not among those who consider businessmen to be low-moral, low-culture characters, very often quite the contrary. But on the other hand, it is true that in the quasi-totalitarian, neo-classical *'pensée unique'*, all forms of business are reduced to the one model of the neo-classical firm. I suggest that a law firm does not correspond to that model. Since too many rights can destroy the law, since more litigation is not necessarily good law, since more law and less politics is not necessarily good for civilized public order, the level of legal output affects society in a way which is different from the level of production of bread, textiles or even literature. In my view of public order, we don't necessarily want to leave the questions 'how much law', 'how much litigation' to market forces. These are political questions *a priori* and the framework should be set accordingly and therefore should not depend entirely on how effectively lawyers market the product called 'Law' or 'Legal Services'. And this is precisely the difference between law firms and many other businesses. So, a spectacular increase of legal output on the basis of the lawyers' profit motive (also called legalization or judicialization of society) must be valued differently, and must bring about a separate framework of regulation, than a spectacular increase in the sale of a true market commodity.

Given the different surroundings in which lawyers work, and the different sets of rules, control mechanisms and incentives to which they respond, I think it is fair to question whether a legal profession as such still exists.

Do these respective and different practices of lawyers at least still share a common nature? To begin addressing this question, it should be pointed out that there is considerable discussion on the combination in one firm of the practice of law and the offering of services in other fields, such as accountancy, consultancy or lobbying. Law then becomes just one area of the business activity, intertwined with and sometimes probably hard to distinguish from other areas. In a regulatory practice for instance, it is hard to distinguish law from lobbying.

Does the profession of law still exist? Law increasingly a process not a body of principles

The kinds of law one comes across in the various practice environments are very different and sometimes have no overlap at all. Are they at least related to a body called 'law'? This is to presuppose that there is still such a body as a fabric of coherent rules and principles which help to organize state and society and which govern the relations among citizens. And this must, alas, also be questioned. Law has become very often a question of process, without a link to any principles and rules of substance. It has, of course, been used by social-democratic governments as a mere instrument for re-distribution of wealth and income, without any regard to the original meaning of legal concepts or the coherence of the system. It is unbelievable how much lousy legislation, even from a purely legalistic point of view, has been adopted in the past, and the situation is not improving. This kind of legislation has affected, as a cancer, the entire body of law, and greatly contributed to its disintegration, to a point where the legal practitioner is rarely able to provide a client with a reasonable degree of legal certainty.

Now that governments no longer have the money to spread around, new 'fundamental rights' are called into existence, which give individuals or groups special rights which they can exercise against other individuals or groups, or existing rights (eg, damages under tort law) are expanded to obtain the same result. It amounts to a distribution of legal weapons to fight a civil war. It also amounts to taking the state and the legislator out of the game since most of these new rights are grounded in constitutions or in treaties protecting human rights, for example the European Convention on Human Rights or the new EU Treaty of Amsterdam.

As law disintegrates so does lawyers' loyalty to law

The impact on the practitioners of law is, of course, considerable. Given the disintegration of the body of law, the second loyalty disappears. We see it replaced by a self-serving loyalty to the 'legal process', particularly then when elected authorities might have the reckless idea of putting the law and lawyers back in their proper place. In this new environment lawyers are able to fully identify with the 'rights' of their clients, without the ballast of 'the law'. As any link between law and morality will have been cut as well, and as the law will provide its own morality, the doors will be wide open for very lucrative lawyers' crusades. Lawyers can then become virtually unrestrained hired guns, organizing the legal equivalent of civil wars in order to obtain transfers of resources from one individual or group to another, purely on the basis of legal process, networks, friendly courts and, of course, power.

Law should be law not a means of social engineering

This seems like a far-fetched vision? Sure it is. But the problem is that all the signs seem to point in that direction, at least in Europe.

The unreasoned ease with which the practice of law is considered to be like any other business, seizing all 'business opportunities', indicates that the legal minds are open and prepared for such an evolution. Moreover, the European Union and the 'global civil society', the legitimate representation of which is claimed by the United Nations, make extensive use of legal instruments in their attack on national sovereignty. Supranational law interferes increasingly in matters which have always been deemed to be within the realm of national law. In addition, from a legal system among states, international law has developed into an instrument which is used to intervene directly in national law on behalf of individuals and groups considered worthy of special protection, thereby claiming precedence over national law, even including constitutional law. Apart from undermining national sovereignty, this development greatly contributes to the dispersion of arbitrary legal rights and hence to the 'legalization' of civil society and the banalization of the role of politics, and thus of democracy.

Is there a way back? Should we go back? Back to where? It isn't difficult in principle. We must indeed go back – or forward, does it matter? – to a society where law is law, and not an instrument of social engineering nor a gun for civil warfare or power plays, where lawyers are lawyers with a double loyalty, where law firms are law firms and not time-selling devices.

The way forward: re-nationalize law

First, I would like to mention something which we should *not* do. Because of the close connection between law, the exercise of the legal profession, and the way nation-based societies are organized, states should not give up their control over the regulation of the practice of law in favour of some supranational body such as the European Union or the World Trade Organization. We have discussed the dangers of cutting the connection between law and the practice of law and the history-based institutional fabric of society. Giving up the possibility to control the way law is practised will inevitably affect the law itself and hence the organization of society. I see no good reason to reinforce the current of the legalized global society, ultimately replacing nation-based law by global power plays. In an intelligent way, and with the greatest possible openness of mind, we should perhaps re-nationalize the law and the role it plays in society. Most certainly, the absurdity of the automatic precedence of international over national law should be ended.

And then, the really difficult task begins. That task is at the same time political, cultural and moral. We should take our destiny back into our hands. The forces of civilization should be restored. We should bring back some historical perspective, show why a concept of public order makes sense and what that may entail, even if it includes a vision of the legal profession as a different business, which may greatly upset those who wrongly identify a market economy with a predatory global society in which conflicts would be 'managed' by lawyers finally liberated from the burden of democracy, law or a legal profession.

6

Character, virtue, vocationalism and the state of the medical profession

an American view

John P Bunker

Why has the profession of medicine been challenged at the time of its greatest success?

The power, authority and autonomy of the medical profession, unquestioned in the past, have been under mounting challenge for at least a quarter of a century, a challenge that seems unlikely to lessen. The same quarter of a century has seen steady growth in the capacity to cure and to provide symptomatic relief. It has been accompanied by the development of sophisticated methods to evaluate the effectiveness of therapy and to document its limitations. It is ironic that at a time when medicine's successes are manifold and rapidly expanding, it should be subjected to its greatest criticisms since the beginning of the nineteenth century. I will argue that it is the medical profession's signal achievements in self-examination, focusing more on failures than on successes, that has invited such critical attacks. I will also argue that confrontation with its critics has further strengthened the central elements of professionalism: that the ensuing effort to document, to explain and to justify medical practice has been a strong force for self-improvement.

The elements that demarcate professions, as summarized by the American sociologist Eliot Freidson,[1] are a unique body of knowledge and skills that justify the sole authority to determine 'the qualifications and number of those to be trained for practice', 'the terms, conditions, and goals of practice itself', 'the ethical and technical criteria by which

... practices are evaluated'; and that justify 'the exclusive right to exercise discipline over their members'. To these should be added the right to a major but not unique authority over and responsibility for the organization and delivery of services. It is against these prerogatives and responsibilities that the medical profession should be judged.

Medical science and its information base

It is the quality of the unique and exclusive body of scientific knowledge that has been subject to some of its earliest attacks. The early attacks came primarily from doctors themselves. Oliver Wendell Holmes, Professor at Harvard Medical School and father of the famous jurist, wrote, in the mid-nineteenth century, that 'if the whole *materia medica*, as now used, could be sunk to the bottom of the sea, it would be all the better for mankind, and all the worse for the fishes.'[2] A hundred years later, the Dean of Harvard Medical School said, during graduation ceremonies, that 'half of what you are taught as medical students will in ten years have been shown to be wrong, and the trouble is, none of your teachers knows which half.'[3] And as recently as 20 years ago, the distinguished clinical scholar, Lewis Thomas, wrote that

> We have come a long way indeed, just to have learned enough to become conscious of our ignorance. It is not so bad a thing to be totally ignorant; the hard thing is to be part way along toward real knowledge, far enough to be aware of being ignorant.[4]

A milestone in the effort to overcome this ignorance was the publication of the 1971 Rock Carling Lecture entitled *Effectiveness and Efficiency.*[5] Written by A L Cochrane, former Director of the Medical Research Council Epidemiology Unit in Cardiff, it was a call to the profession for the evaluation of the evidence underlying the practice of medicine; from his slender volume has grown an international programme of research designed to determine the effectiveness of medical procedures, known as the Cochrane Collaboration, and, indirectly, a growing recognition that medical science has today advanced to a point that it is now possible to practice medicine that is 'evidence based'.

In the 1970s, however, the need for evidence of effectiveness seemed less urgent than addressing the possibility that medicine might do harm, and there were widespread inquiries by the medical profession into iatronic illness, including adverse drug reactions and harm from surgery. This provided ammunition for a spate of critics, led by Ivan Illich, to claim that medicine may not only be ineffective, but may do more harm than good.[6] While Illich's claims are, and were even at the time of first publication in 1975, unbalanced and often untrue, the cudgel has been taken up by many others. Stung and feeling ill-used, the medical profession had only itself to blame. We had been so preoccupied with the problems of medical care that we failed to put them in the context of the good that medicine does and that we assumed could be taken for granted.

Medical contribution to health low 1900-1945, high thereafter

The belief that the contribution of modern medicine to people's lives is either marginal or downright harmful provides the philosophical rationale for the concerted effort of those involved in health policy to curtail the power and independence of the profession. It is therefore appropriate to examine such claims in more detail.

Medicine's contribution to health has been generally judged on the basis of its effect on death rates and life-expectancy. Judged on this basis alone, medicine's contribution during the first half of this century was a very small one. Medicine contributed at most two of the approximately 25 years of increased life-expectancy that were recorded between 1900 and 1950 in the UK and in North America. This was a period in which acute infectious diseases, and their control, dominated public health and the practice of medicine. Public health measures were responsible for the sharp decline in infectious disease experienced early in the century, most of which had been achieved before the introduction of many of the vaccines, and well before the availability of antibiotics. Viewed only from the perspective of the acute infectious diseases, the epidemiologist Thomas McKeown, writing over 20 years ago, concluded that medicine's role as a determinant of health is a very small one,[7] and McKeown's conclusions have coloured most subsequent thinking.

In the 50 years following the Second World War, there has been an explosion of new and effective medical treatments, many of which lead to substantial improvements in health. Life-expectancy has risen a further seven years in England and in America, of which medicine can now be shown to have contributed three.[8] The five years of increased life-expectancy attributed to medical care during the century is considered by some to represent a small achievement. That it is in fact a large one can be appreciated by the fact that it is equivalent, on average, to a halving of the death rate at every age throughout life.

So, medicine matters, after all. Nonetheless, this does not in itself legitimise the unconstrained professional freedom for doctors to organize their affairs as they wish, irrespective of the need to justify their actions or provide the type of medical care that the public requires.

Three factors have become increasingly important in recent years: the need to demonstrate objectively the benefits of medical intervention, the ability of the profession to regulate itself, and the question of cost.

Measuring the outcome of care

Assessing the results of treatment has received intermittent attention since the beginning of the century. The early efforts to measure the outcome of treatment were tentative and had little impact on treatment. The orthopaedic surgeon E A Codman's proposal in 1914 to measure what he called the 'end-results' of surgery[9] was rejected by the ultra-conservative doctors at the Massachusetts General Hospital in Boston, but his manifesto was not forgotten; in 1952 the American Surgical Association began publishing the minutes of its Committee on Unnecessary Operations,[10] a forerunner of today's inquiries into the 'appropriateness' of care.

My own concerns with the outcomes of surgery were raised during a year of sabbatical study in 1966 at the Westminster Hospital in London. I was impressed by how similar medical and surgical practice was in the United Kingdom and in the United States, and yet, in many ways, how different. I found, for example, that patients in the UK were half as likely, on average, to undergo surgery in a given year as were patients in the USA.[11] Life-expectancy was slightly greater in the UK, so more surgery in the USA did not mean that more lives were being saved. Perhaps the quality of life was better served by surgery in the USA, but there were no data at that time by which to demonstrate it. Quality of life as an important basis for assessing the appropriateness of medical and surgical care is now widely recognized and its measurement has become an integral component of clinical trials.

It was startling to observe such differences in the amount of care provided between countries. Even more dramatic was the demonstration of large variations within a single country.[12] It was the recognition of these 'small area variations' in the United States that prompted Congress in 1989 to establish the Agency for Health Care Policy and Research for support of research in the measurement and evaluation of the outcomes of medical and surgical care.[13] This marked the beginning of the American 'outcomes movement', dedicated to the documentation of the results of medical and surgical treatment.

Peer review and discipline

The outcomes of medical and surgical care, as well as the amount of care provided, vary widely, and when the outcome is poor, close scrutiny is called for to determine whether the poor outcome was the result of negligence or incompetence. It was initially for this purpose that the medical audit was initiated by the doctors themselves and became established as standard hospital procedure. Audit was at the outset perceived as punitive, a process of weeding out 'bad apples'. And while it has been an essential tool for identifying a small number of doctors whose care is sub-standard, its potential for involving an entire medical establishment in improving the quality of care has only recently been recognized and implemented in a programme of 'continuous quality improvement':[14] defects in the process of care are identified, procedures for their correction proposed and tested, and, if successful, implemented.

The movement towards involvement of an entire medical establishment in quality improvement has already taken hold in medicolegal accountability, hospitals and medical groups increasingly being held responsible for the outcome of care within the institution. A recommendation to formalize this as a medicolegal principle of 'enterprise liability' or corporate responsibility was introduced as a key component of the Clinton Administration's 1993 malpractice reform package.[15] By shifting responsibility from individual doctors to the 'enterprise' in which they are participants, incentives are created for doctors, other health professionals, and non-medical support staff to work together in teams to improve the whole process of care. Trust and compassion, its proponents argued, would be promoted, and,

> trust and compassion will remain essential to successful health care delivery, and must be assured by both the preservation of traditional ethical principles and the development of a "new professionalism" based more on social responsibility and less on guild autonomy.[16]

The proposal for enterprise liability was strongly opposed by the American Medical Association and by the insurance carriers and was dropped by the Clinton Administration from its final proposal for health-care reforms.

The rising cost of medical care

Underlying the movement to measure the outcomes and benefits of medical care is the question, are they worth the escalating costs? To begin to answer this question, we need an understanding of the economics of medicine, as well as measurement of benefits. This need remains unfulfilled, for the debate over economic policy and medicine has been carried out in ignorance or neglect of elementary economic theory as well as disregard of medical productivity. The economic theory is either unknown or deliberately ignored by our governments and rarely explained to the public.

The economic principle is simply that as efficiency and productivity increase in many areas of industry, time and resources become available for other enterprises. Automation and computerization have resulted in enormous increases in productivity requiring a much smaller workforce and, in the process, have freed up labour and resources that could be made available for medical care and other labour-intensive activities.[17] It is not a shortage that constrains investment in medicine, the American economist William Baumol argues. It is simply a question of how the public chooses to spend the resources and money that an increasingly productive economy continues to make available.

Baumol's explanation accounts for an important part of the increased cost of medical care. In addition, some of the escalating price of medical care can be attributed to an ageing population, wasteful administrative costs, defensive medicine (particularly in the United States), and expensive care for the terminally ill.[18] But 'the main cost driver is new technology and its capacity to increase the capabilities of medicine'.

An informed public might well choose to pay for increased medical benefits. Levels of funding in the National Health Service have surely not been set in a way that might allow the public to make that choice, nor is there an explicit mechanism to adjust funding to respond to increased medical productivity. In the United States funding has, in the past, floated upwards as new technologies have been introduced; today all this is changing as fee-for-service is being replaced by pre-payment and capitation in NHS-like health maintenance organizations (HMOs). The HMOs are increasingly owned or controlled by insurance companies, with managed care the dominant form of organization and the doctor a salaried employee.

Can professionalism survive in the marketplace?

In the United States, the doctor has become bound to his institution, fiscally and contractually as well as socially and legally. Increasingly it has become necessary, if they are to continue in practice, for doctors to accept salaried employment in HMOs. As employees, doctors are inescapably and directly subject to managerial control; and they are also inevitably, willingly or unwillingly, pawns in the competitive restructuring of health care. This surely has weakened the autonomy of individual doctors and is a serious threat to professionalism, ironically at a time when essential components of professionalism are gaining in strength. Freidson, viewing this threat, worries that professionalism in American medicine and 'the flexible discretionary judgement that is necessary to adapt services to individual [patients'] needs' may be crushed between the forces of government regulation on one side and the market forces of competition on the other.[19]

If autonomy of the individual doctor is threatened by managerial control and by competition in the marketplace, surely it had already become an anachronism with the advance of medical science. As J R Hampton editorialised in 'The end of clinical freedom',[20]

> Clinical freedom was the right of doctors to do whatever in their opinion was best for their patients ... medical care must [now] be limited to what is of proved value ...

But while the autonomy and clinical freedom of the individual doctor may have become a thing of the past, the autonomy of the profession, and of groups of professionals, need not be sacrificed. What has been lost in individual freedom can be, and to some extent is being gained as standards of clinical practice become established on a more scientific basis. The autonomy that each person loses is given to his or her own colleagues or, as Freidson says, to 'fellow professionals in a professionally controlled system rather than subordination to those trained solely as managers'.[21]

Such a professionally controlled system is within reach. To be fully realized it will need leadership from the medical profession together with nurture by and collaboration with government and corporate management. Nurture will need to take the form of acceptance of the medical profession and of individual practitioners as equal partners rather than simply as 'highly paid producers of services to be managed like a collective bargaining unit' (as Henry J Kaiser first considered the doctors he hired to provide medical care for his California shipyard workers during the Second World War[22]). The Kaiser Health Plan currently offers several million subscribers medical care on a prepaid basis and resembles the NHS in many ways. How a balance of authority and responsibility between doctors and management was fought for and achieved, provides a model for current efforts to reconcile conflicting interests in the UK as well as in the USA.

There are many obstacles to such a balance of authority and responsibility that have been erected in the new form of managed care plans in the United States. These include financial arrangements that provide strong incentives for the doctor to limit the provision of care and access to specialist consultation; utilisation review limiting the doctor's freedom to treat and prescribe; and so-called gag rules, confidentiality clauses in the doctor's employment contract that prohibit disclosure of information that might damage the reputation of the managed care plan. Any and all of the above are serious threats to patients' trust in the doctor as their advocate.[23]

Managed care as a dominant force in medical care in the United States is in an early and rapidly changing stage, and it is much too soon to say how it will turn out. In one scenario, some doctors

> undoubtedly will find themselves with unprecedented opportunities to put their training to work for their patients. Freed by capitation to innovate in health care delivery, supported by professional management and state of the art information systems, newly sensitive to consumer wishes, and spurred by the example of competing organizations, these physicians will deliver care of unprecedented quality and efficiency ... This result seems most likely to occur when savvy, enlightened purchasers with highly educated workforces are able to identify and form partnerships with well-managed provider organizations that employ competent, conscientious physicians.[24]

In an alternative scenario, however, less 'savvy' patients

> may find themselves enrolled in health care organizations that employ deprofessionalized physicians who are more responsive to the administrative and economic controls of their employers than to the needs and wishes of individual patients. Such physicians, and the organizations for which they work, may deliver care that is far inferior in quality and efficiency to what they would provide under non-competitive circumstances.[25]

Membership in health maintenance organizations now exceeds 50 million and is growing rapidly; but HMOs are already facing a strong backlash from physicians angry at loss of autonomy and income, and from patients dissatisfied with restraints as to choice of provider and access to care. The backlash is taking the form of

> federal and state legislation, lawsuits naming HMOs as defendants, statewide electoral initiative drives, horror stories in the mass media, the emergence of physician-run HMOs to compete with HMOs run by corporate executives, and a drive for medical savings accounts to draw patients away from HMOs.[26]

It is ironic that the current HMO movement should appear in the United States at a time long after a highly successful and professional model of prepaid group practice had become well established, notably the Kaiser Permanente Health Plan, the Group Health Cooperative of Puget Sound, and the Park Nicollet Medical Foundation in Minneapolis/St Paul. Should this model become the norm, it should again be possible for patients to 'have access to services purely on the basis of clinical criteria', and for doctors to 'stop thinking about money and devote themselves single-mindedly to their patients'.[27]

A few years ago I asked 'Can professionalism survive in the Marketplace?'[28] I believe that it can, but only if: corporate medical plans and government recognize doctors as equal partners; medical practice is clearly based on cooperation and not on competition; and if doctors, for their part, function as a unified profession speaking with a single voice. In the much quoted words of Benjamin Franklin, 'we must indeed all hang together, or most assuredly, we shall all hang separately' (remark made to John Hancock at the signing of the Declaration of Independence, 4 July, 1776).

7

Successful but devalued:
the medical profession – a British view

James Le Fanu

Despite medicine's success, doctors demoralized

Any account of the current state of the medical profession has to come
to grips with a most perplexing paradox. The achievements of medicine
in the 50 years since the Second World War rank as one of the most
sustained epochs of human endeavour since the Renaissance. So
dramatically successful has been the assault on disease, it is now almost
impossible to imagine the world in 1945 when polio, diphtheria and
tetanus were rife, tuberculosis was untreatable, there were no drugs
for the treatment of Parkinson's, rheumatoid arthritis or schizophrenia
or indeed most of the diseases in medical text books, a time before
open heart surgery, transplantation and test-tube babies. These – and
many other – developments have had a profoundly beneficial effect,
freeing people from the fear of illness and untimely death, permitting
them for the first time in human history to live out their natural lifespan,
while significantly ameliorating the chronic disabilities associated with
age.

This success has transformed medicine from a cottage industry into
a vast enterprise, employing millions and costing billions. In Britain
the NHS budget has risen from £437 million in 1949 to £42,000
million in 1995 and the numbers employed have more than doubled
to over a million. These figures, impressive as they are, fade into
insignificance when compared to the United States where 'health' is a
trillion-dollar business.

Yet despite all this which has made medicine much the largest and
politically significant of all the liberal professions, doctors are not just
unhappy but, if recent surveys are to be believed, variously bored,
disillusioned and demoralized. Had they been asked in the 1950s

whether they found the practice of their profession fulfilling, they would have been baffled that anyone should have bothered to enquire. Nowadays 50 per cent claim that, if given their time over again, they would choose another occupation.[1]

It is only sensible to view the results of such surveys with a healthy scepticism, who – after all – is really happy with their lot? Nonetheless doctors should at least be content to be part of a profession that not only has achieved so much over the last half century, but offers high salaries, security of employment and prestige.

The reasons for this disillusion are complex. John Bunker in the previous chapter points to several, most notably the profession's loss of autonomy over the last 10 years as it has been forced to cede power, losing out in Britain to a new managerial elite and in the United States to the influential Health Maintenance Organizations (HMOs).

My approach to this matter is to take an historical view and seek to trace the causes of the changing fortunes of the profession and, in particular, how this relates to the intellectual and moral basis of medical practice – 'professionalism'. So it is appropriate to start by describing some of its salient characteristics.

Features of professionalism – expertise, judgement, beneficence, integrity, independence

First, medicine – as with all the other professions – has a knowledge base. After prolonged training doctors, hopefully, know more about the medical sciences than non-doctors and are thus in a position to diagnose what is wrong and know how to put it right. But this 'knowledge base' is more than an accumulation of facts because there are many aspects of medicine – particularly the causation of a disease – that remain obscure, while the question of what is 'the right thing to do' in any instance is profoundly influenced by experience and clinical judgement. Doctors must be able to accommodate these grey areas of uncertainty when reaching their decisions, while also possessing an emotional intelligence that can cope with the misfortunes of people's lives.

Secondly, doctors earn their living like everyone else by providing a service, but its distinguishing feature is that it is based on a special personal relationship. As Robin Downie, Professor of Philosophy at Glasgow University, explains: 'The object of the professional attitude is the client conceived in terms of *vulnerability*, there is an inequality of power.'[2] The patient is at the mercy of the doctor's greater knowledge and is therefore vulnerable to being exploited by, for example, being over-treated for minor ailments in order for the doctor to collect his fee. This danger is minimized by the doctor's 'professional attitude' – 'a desire to be of assistance' – often called 'beneficence'. Professor Downie continues:

> The pathology of "beneficence" is "paternalism", the tendency to decide for individuals what they ought to decide for themselves ... and the antidote to paternalism is a sense of justice and honesty which I call "integrity".[3]

The third defining feature of professionalism is independence. Doctors can only carry out their duties pursuing the best interests of their patients if they are free of outside interference that might adversely influence that judgement – particularly interference caused by the demands of state or commerce. The central feature of independence is that doctors are 'free agents' – free to practise in a way they consider most appropriate, without their activities being scrutinized by others.

These principles of professionalism are not something that is tacked on to the practice of medicine to make it respectable. Rather they are intrinsic to how it works. And if, for any reason, one or other of these principles is transgressed then 'the system' fails.

The failure of doctors to adhere to these principles, plus spiralling costs led to demands for political control

My argument, in a nutshell, is as follows. Doctors during the 1970s, failed to adhere to the principles of professionalism. In the US they failed to 'act with integrity', but rather over-investigated and over-treated their patients to maximize their income. In Britain some, a minority, abused the freedom conferred by their independent status within the health service to engage in private practice at the expense of their NHS commitments. These lapses in professionalism, along with the spiralling costs of health care, generated the political imperative to control the activities of the profession, as a result of which they have been forced to cede a measure of their independence to a managerialist culture which in turn is a significant contributory factor to their demoralization.

Some sense of the current discontent can be gained by a comparison of the current atmosphere in one medical institution, my *alma mater*, the Royal London Hospital, with how it struck me when I arrived as a medical student back in 1971.

The Royal London – founded in 1740 – is located in the most impoverished part of the capital – the East End – which has been home to succeeding generations of immigrants fleeing tyranny and oppression in Russia and Central Europe. When I arrived in 1971, the core of the consultant staff consisted of a group of physicians and surgeons who had themselves been medical students and junior doctors at the London during the War years. Then, the hospital, by virtue of its location close to the docks, was at the centre of the Blitz and was struck altogether eight times by high explosives and on innumerable occasions by incendiary devices. Sir John Ellis, a medical student at the time and subsequently Dean of the Medical School, recalls the atmosphere in which

> particular incidents are seen with startling clarity ... the ground floor wards full of sick patients, quiet enough to hear the drone of planes, preceding the noise of guns and bombs ... dark stairs up which porters and students stumbled carrying casualties on stretchers ... [4]

The purpose of this historical diversion is to emphasize how in John Ellis's words, 'those who knew the London at that time developed a very close personal attachment to it, as sailors feel for their ship'.

The old hospital in which everyone knew everyone and all knew their place

Profoundly influenced by these experiences, the consultants at the London in 1971 were bound by a strong sense of loyalty to their hospital which in essence they controlled with the help of the House Governor and Matron. They had their 'own' junior staff and their 'own' wards staffed by their 'own' nurses. After a morning ward round, 'the Chief' might drop across the road to see a couple of private patients in the private block before meeting his fellow consultants for lunch in their own dining room. They would discuss the affairs of 'their' hospital to whose best interest they were deeply committed.

It was a hierarchical, authoritarian system that essentially ran itself, but central to its success was the personal nature of the working relationships between consultants, junior staff and the nurses, in which everyone knew everyone else and everyone knew their place.

After qualifying, I had little further contact with the Royal London but returned in 1996 at the invitation of one of the consultant staff. The consultants' dining room had long been demolished and now all grades of staff share a communal dining room. The consultants still stick together, sharing a table and, after my *bona fides* as a former student, had been established, had no reservations in filling me in about the changes over the last decade.

Now, controlled by managerial class, doctors just employees

They were no longer 'in charge', rather the hospital is controlled by a new managerial class – an administrative elite headed by a Chief Executive assisted by a galaxy of financial officers, contracts managers and other trappings of private enterprise such as public relations persons. The consultants had no formalized dealings with this new elite whose most distinguishing feature was their number. The House Governor and Matron had been replaced by a cast of hundreds. Now surgeons were told how many operations they were allowed to do – and on whom – (the patients of fund-holding GPs being given priority) while physicians were constrained over the number of new patients they could see. More seriously, they felt they had lost their little fiefdoms, their power bases in the wards. As far as the new management was concerned, the consultants were little different from any other employees in the hospital and so, in the name of rationalisation, they had lost their 'own' wards with their 'own' nursing staff. Their patients were scattered across the hospital making it difficult to keep in touch or have a say in how they were looked after. The nurses could be friendly and helpful (but not invariably as the prevailing nursing ideology is that they should no longer be 'subservient' to doctors) but the hierarchical chain of responsibility had been broken and with it the tradition of the daily ward round and the confidential discussion between staff which had, in the past, promoted the best interests of their patients.

Ties of loyalty broken

And what does all this mean? The hospital had been atomized, the ties of loyalty that had bound the various professional groups to each other and to the institution in which they worked had been broken. The new arrangement, I was told, was much less efficient than that which it had replaced and, in particular, it was much more difficult to ensure that things were done properly. They remembered how it had been and had watched their power and influence ebb away. All changes had been for the worse and the élan of the hospital had been lost.

There are obvious limitations to such an impressionistic description of the changing fortunes of my former teaching hospital but, in broad outline, I am sure it is accurate.

In USA doctors employed and managed by HMOs

Before examining the causes and consequences of these events in Britain, it is appropriate to take a brief look across the Atlantic to see how doctors have been faring 'over there'. 'The practice of medicine as we have known it all our lives is gone', observed Robert Brame in his Presidential address to the American Association of Obstetricians and Gynaecologists in 1994.[5]

> We will lose our professionalism and our autonomy, we will be paid less than we are worth and will be directed in our daily activities by criteria that are based on considerations other than patients' well-being. The good physicians will be the ones who save the greatest amount of money, the bad ones who spend the most and a third party will make most of our decisions for us.

Historically, US medicine has been based on the principal of fee for service. You go to see the doctor, he charges you for his services, the fees are then recoupable from your private health insurance. Medical care is expensive, so health insurance premiums are high, too high for many on middle incomes who then have to cut back on other areas of personal expenditure, and much too high for 35 million citizens who have no insurance cover at all.

The situation has been transformed over the last 10 years by the rise of the Health Maintenance Organization (HMO) which has made health care affordable again to most Americans. HMOs charge a relatively modest fee for which the subscriber gets the attention of the physicians in their employ and hospital care at a hospital with which the HMO has negotiated a contract. Here is how it works:

> We now hear of managed care organizations coming into town and demanding contracts that pay specialists 20 per cent of their previous charges in exchange for guaranteed volume. If the physician protests, the organization can always give the 'business' to someone else. Physicians with expensive practices find themselves in the argot of the day 'deselected'. Sometimes they are indeed guilty of causing unwarranted expenditure and of wanton over-abuse of resources. But sometimes they are guilty only of treating the chronically and severely ill and therefore costly patients.[6]

Clearly then, if the HMOs are to offer financially-accessible health care they must have control over what physicians in their employ are doing and, in particular, how many expensive tests they request and what treatments they decide are necessary. In essence then, doctors have to a greater or lesser extent lost their freedom to practise as they wish, and have become in increasing numbers employees of HMOs or private health care organizations to whose managers and accountants they are responsible for their actions. In summary, doctors on the other side of the Atlantic have, over the last 10 years, been knocked off their pedestals losing a considerable measure of their independence – which some might argue is no bad thing.

The need to control comes from cost of successful post-war medicine

The root cause of these developments is, paradoxically, the extraordinary success of post-war medicine. The problem with the introduction of wonderful new drugs and treatments – open heart surgery, curing cancer, replacing hips, test-tube babies and the like – is that they cost money. And the more widely available these treatments become to an increasingly ageing population, the greater the cost, which in Britain is a burden on the Exchequer, and in the United States has been reflected in ever-higher and, to many, financially punitive health insurance premiums. When doctors had only a limited range of options – as in the first decade after the War – then the responsibility for spending the monies available could reasonably be left to the discretion of those making the therapeutic decisions – usually the doctors. So the NHS in Britain got by with the simplest of all structures where the money trickled downwards from the Treasury to the individual hospitals and the consultants were the dominant influence in deciding how it should be spent.

But as the NHS bill grew incrementally, it was only natural that someone should begin to enquire how these funds were spent, and ask whether they were being spent in the best possible way and how one could measure in a meaningful way the results of this expenditure. Gradually it became clear that this situation where doctors were quite unaccountably responsible for billions of pounds of public expenditure could no longer be tolerated. They may well have been doing a good job – and indeed the British health service was much the most cost effective in the western world, generating more services per millions of pounds spent than any other. But with an escalating budget year by year, the argument for tighter political control became ever stronger, which inevitably required that the power and autonomy of the doctors would have to be curtailed.

Demand for control fuelled by professional abuse by doctors
Further, politicians and those responsible for health policy had other motives for wishing to clip the profession's wings and here doctors really had only themselves to blame for their subsequent misfortunes. In increasing numbers they were failing to fulfil their NHS obligations in favour of making considerable amounts of money privately, and their independence and autonomy was such that there were absolutely no sanctions to prevent them from doing so. Some surgeons, it was alleged, deliberately kept their NHS waiting list long so as to encourage patients to 'go private'. This highlighted a related problem, the absence of any mechanisms to direct or encourage doctors to do what needed to be done. Hernias are common but boring and rather than getting on with repairing them, surgeons preferred to tackle something more challenging. As a result, patients with hernias vegetated on the waiting list for years even though all they needed to get back to work was a speedy 15-minute operation.

It is difficult to know how widespread such abuses were, but there is no doubt they became much more frequent in Britain from 1974 onwards after Barbara Castle, as Labour's Minister for Health, forced NHS hospitals to restrict the number of private beds, as a result of which large US private health care companies moved in to London and started building private hospitals. As a result, consultants could no longer see their private patients as part of their routine NHS work – fitted in between the morning ward round and lunch – they now had to travel to see their patients in the new private hospitals which necessarily loosened their ties of loyalty to the NHS. Around this time the newly oil-rich Arabs started arriving in London for their private medical care and, encouraged by the managers of the private hospitals to charge much higher fees, the attractions of making large sums of money in salubrious surroundings proved very tempting.

Clearly it was wrong that consultants should be drawing an NHS salary for work they were not doing and, in a properly functioning, self-regulatory profession, those who did so should have been the subject of disciplinary proceedings (or at least the active disapproval of colleagues) but they were not. As health economist Donald Light points out:

British surgeons and anaesthetists are short changing their NHS patients in order to stuff their pockets with gold. In the process they compromise the public trust on which the NHS operates. Specifically the public pays them well to make that effort but they only put in three to six hours a week at the operating table ... In addition a third of them slip out of attending their fixed commitment sessions ... [7]

The standard official response from organizations such as the BMA to such criticisms is that they apply to 'only a minority'. Most doctors do much more than their NHS contracts require. This may well be correct but the failure to discipline those responsibile for such abuses is clearly a powerful argument in favour of doctors being 'managed'.

In USA too many doctors pursuing too few patients – over-treatment

In the United States, the need for some form of control over health expenditure and the activities of doctors was even greater. The problem was that there were just too many doctors, in particular far too many specialists, pursuing too few patients on a fee for service basis. The obvious – and only – way for doctors to maximize their income in these circumstances was to over-investigate and over-treat their patients and overcharge third parties such as Medicare who foot the bill. In the United States, no headache is too trivial or transient that it does not merit an MRI scan to exclude an underlying brain tumour, no degree of narrowing of the coronary arteries too insignificant to justify a bypass operation.

The public had no alternative other than to pay for this medical incontinence with ever-increasing health insurance premiums and those who could not afford them did without. As Robert Brame observed in his already-cited Presidential address

Physicians remain among the highest paid members of all occupations in the land at a time when medical bills of all kinds have an impact on the lifestyle of everyone except the superrich, and against a background of 37 million who have no health insurance. It would be juvenile to believe that we are not the target of public scorn and prime candidates for a visit from our nemesis.[8]

The new managerialism

In the late 1980s on both sides of the Atlantic, the nemesis finally arrived in the form of managerialism – bureaucratic managerialism in Britain, HMOs and private corporate managerialism in the United States. Before examining the impact of managerialism on the state of the profession – already illustrated by the reflections of the consultants at the Royal London Hospital – it is worth considering the degree to which doctors, by transgressing the principles of professionalism, have only themselves to blame.

In Britain, a minority of doctors abused the privilege of autonomy conferred on them by the state at the founding of the National Health Service. The contract was simple. Consultants would be paid a handsome salary and provided with the facilities to practise medicine – hospitals, junior staff and so on – in return for their skills and commitment, but the precise manner in which they conducted their lives was left to their own discretion. The outcome was a double betrayal. Individual doctors reneged on their NHS commitments while the profession's regulatory bodies such as the General Medical Council abused the right of professional self-regulation conferred by Parliament by failing to discipline those responsible.

In the United States the betrayal of professionalism was more serious. The over-investigation and over-treatment of patients, by exposing them to the hazards of unnecessary medication and surgery, represents precisely the exploitation of the vulnerable that the principles of 'beneficence' ('a desire to be of assistance') and integrity ('a sense of justice and honesty') are intended to avoid.

The doctors' nemesis – when it came in the late 1980s – took different forms on the two sides of the Atlantic. In the United States 'managed care' as exemplified by the Health Maintenance Organization, controlled costs, making health care affordable again by the simple expedient of strictly supervising medical decisions. In Britain the nemesis came in two stages. In 1983, Roy Griffiths, managing director of Sainsbury's reviewed – at the government's request – management structures within the National Health Service and came to his famous conclusion – 'if Florence Nightingale were carrying her lamp through the corridors of the NHS today she would almost certainly be searching for the people in charge'. The NHS, he suggested, should be managed, somebody other than the doctors should be in charge of initiating cost improvement programmes, evaluating treatments, and holding the consultants to account for their results.[9] This, however, was only a minor prelude to the tidal wave that hit the profession six years later in 1989 – the Conservative Government's NHS reforms based on the principles of an 'internal market' in health.

The consequences of managerialism in the UK – disillusionment

In the concluding part of this chapter I will focus on the impact of the 1989 NHS reforms. It is not appropriate here to describe the administrative changes in any detail, but their ostensible intention was to improve the effectiveness of the health service by the introduction of 'competition' with the creation of a 'purchase-provider' split. Here the 'providers' – NHS hospitals – were forced to compete with each other for contracts from 'purchasers' – the health authorities and general practice fund-holders – thus creating the incentive to control their costs and enhance the quality of the service they provided.

The process of negotiating these contracts is complex and time-consuming and thus the most tangible immediate consequence of these reforms was a vast increase in the number of managerial and clerical staff – the ranks of senior managers swelled from 500 to over 20,000 in the five years from 1989 to 1994.

By itself the sudden arrival of this sizeable new managerial elite in hospitals obviously posed a threat to the previously dominant position of the hospital consultants who, in the resulting struggle for power, were roundly defeated. Thus, as the consultants with whom I talked at the Royal London Hospital observed, the deliberations of the doctors' committees were simply ignored. They were deprived – in the name of efficient bed utilization – of their 'own' wards and the fulfilment of their NHS obligations was closely scrutinized.

As a direct consequence, many consultants have either retired early or are looking forward to the day when they can leave the Health Service, observed Norman Browse, former President of the Royal College of Surgeons, who 'has noted a steady deterioration in hospital doctors' morale' since the introduction of the reforms. The main cause, he believes, is 'the lack of clinical independence and the ability to introduce improvements in the services they provide'.[10] A survey of doctors' attitudes to the health service changes concluded:

> They give the impression of being conquered peoples of a once great civilization, suffering indignities and authoritarian brutalities of a barbarian occupying power.[11]

It is necessary to keep an appropriate perspective on such comments. The everyday practice of medicine continues much as it always has and, although doctors may complain of the new arrangements, most have developed a *modus vivendi* where they try and have as little to do with their new masters as possible and get on with their lives as best they can.

There is, however, a lot more to the low morale described by Norman Browse than merely injured *amour propre*. The general verdict on the NHS reforms is that their expense and complexity have made the health service less, rather than more, cost-effective, while the day-to-day running of the hospitals is less efficient due to the decline in standards previously maintained by the hierarchical system of responsibility.

Paradoxically then, the major impression of the new arrangements is that they merely serve to emphasize the virtues of the system that they replaced. It is probable that in time doctors will regain their previous power and authority. They remain after all the best educated, most coherent and most effective group within the NHS. It would be good to think that they may have learnt the lessons of experience of the last 10 years that the privileges of their position come with specific moral obligations that should be observed. Perhaps they will, perhaps they will not.

Notes and references

Chapter 2

1. John Henry Newman, *The Idea of a University*, New York: Chelsea House, 1983, pp 40, 89-90, 91-2, 107, 123, 134-6.
2. Newman, op cit, p 157.
3. Bruce Truscot, *Red Brick University*, Harmondsworth: Penguin, 1951, pp 65, 78-9/ Bruce Truscot was the pseudonym of Edgar Allison Peers, Gilmour Professor of Spanish at Liverpool University. The 1951 edition of *Red Brick University* was a revised version of two earlier books, *Red Brick University* (1943) and *These Vital Days* (1945).
4. Lord Robbins, *The University in the Modern World*, London: Macmillan, 1966, pp 1-16.
5. Harold Perkin, *The Rise of Professional Society: England since 1880*, London: Routledge, 1989, p 369.
6. Bernice Martin, *A Sociology of Contemporary Cultural Change*, Oxford: Blackwell, 1981.
7. John Fraser, *America and the Patterns of Chivalry*, Cambridge: Cambridge University Press, 1982.
8. Christopher Lasch, *The Revolt of the Elites and the Betrayal of Democracy*, New York: W W Norton, 1995.
9. Kenneth Minogue, *The Concept of a University*, London: Weidenfeld and Nicolson, 1973, p 65.
10. Lasch, op cit, p 26.
11. Robert Hughes, *The Culture of Complaint*, New York: Oxford University Press, 1993.
12. Harold Bloom, *The Western Canon*, New York: Harcourt Brace, 1994, p 517.
13. *Higher Education*, 2, 1973, p 145.
14. M D Stephens and G W Roderick, eds, *Universities for a Changing World*, Newton Abbot: David and Charles, 1975, p 19.
15. Robert Nisbet, *The Degradation of the Academic Dogma: the University in America 1945-70*, London: Heinemann, 1971.

16. Truscot, op cit, p 103.

Chapter 3
1. Max Weber, *The Sociology of Religion*, London: Methuen, 1963, p 73 (first published as *Religionssoziologie*,1922).
2. Peter Brierley, *Christian England*, London: MARC Europe, 1991, p 55.
3. Grace Davie, *Religion in Britain since 1945: believing without belonging*, Oxford: Blackwell, 1994.
4. Owen Chadwick, *The Victorian Church: Part 1*, 2nd edtn, London: A & C Black, 1970, p 90.
5 Robert Towler and A P M Coxon, *The Fate of the Anglican Clergy*, London: Macmillan, 1979, pp 85-86.
6. Brierly, 1991, op cit, p 147.
7. Roger Homan, *To the Altar of God*, University of Brighton: Education Research Centre, 1995.
8. Ibid, p 23.
9. Towler and Coxon, op cit.

Chapter 6
1. Eliot Freidson, 'How dominant are the professions' in F W Hafferty and J B McKinlay (eds), *The Changing Medical Profession: an International Perspective*, New York and Oxford: Oxford University Press, 1993.
2. M B Strauss, *Familiar Medical Quotations*, Boston, Mass: Little Brown and Company, 1968.
3. Ibid.
4. L Thomas, *Biomedical Science and Human Health: the Long-Range Prospect*, Daedalus, 1997, 106, pp163-171.
5. A L Cochrane, *Effectiveness and Efficiency: Random Reflections on Health Services*, London: The Nuffield Provincial Hospitals Trust, 1972.
6. J P Bunker, 'Ivan Illich and the pursuit of health', *Journal of Health Services and Research Policy*, 1997, 2, pp 56-59.
7. T McKeown, *The role of medicine: dream, mirage, or nemesis?* London: Nuffield Provincial Hospitals Trust, 1976.
8. J P Bunker, 'Medicine matters after all', *Journal of the Royal College of Physicians*, London, 1995, 29, pp 105-112.
9. E A Codman, 'The product of a hospital', *Surgery, Gynecology, Obstetrics*, 1914, 18, pp 491-496.
10. F A Coller, *Minutes of the Committee on Unnecessary Operations*, American Surgical Association, 1952-1960.
11. J P Bunker, 'Surgical manpower: a comparison of operations and surgeons in the United States and in England and Wales', *New England Journal of Medicine*, 1970, 282, pp 135-144.
12. J Wennberg, A Gittelsohn, 'Small area variations in health care delivery', *Science*, 1973, 182, pp 1102-1108.
13. Public Law 101-239, in establishing the Agency for Health Care Policy and

Research, directs the agency 'to enhance the quality, appropriateness, and effectiveness of health care services through a broad program of scientific research and information dissemination' and directed the Secretary of the Department of Health and Human Services to establish 'a program of research on outcomes of health care services and procedures'.

14. D M Berwick, 'Continuous improvement as an ideal in health care', *New England Journal of Medicine*, 1989, 320, pp 53-56.

15. W M Sage, K E Hastings, R A Berenson, 'Enterprise liability for medical malpractice and health care quality improvement', *American Journal of Law and Medicine*, 1994, 20, pp 1-28.

16. Ibid.

17. W J Baumol, 'Social wants and dismal science: the curious case of the climbing costs of health and teaching', *Proceedings of the American Philosophical Society*, 1993, 137, pp 612-637.

18. J P Newhouse, 'An iconoclastic view of health cost containment', *Health Affairs*, 1993, 12 (supp), pp 152-171.

19. E Freidson, 'The centrality of professionalism in health care', *Jurimetrics Journal*, 1990, 30, pp 431-445.

20. J R Hampton, 'The end of clinical freedom', *British Medical Journal*, 1983, 287, pp 1237-1238.

21. E Freidson, *Profession of medicine: a study of the sociology of applied knowledge* (with a new afterword), Chicago, London: University of Chicago Press, 1988.

22. J G Smillie, *Can physicians manage the quality and costs of health care?* New York: McGraw-Hill, 1991.

23. D Mechanic, M Schlesinger, 'The impact of managed care on patients' trust in medical care and their physicians', *Journal of the American Medical Association*, 1996, 275, pp 1693-1697.

24. D Blumenthal, 'Effects of market reforms on doctors and their patients', *Health Affairs*, 1996, 15(2), pp 170-184.

25. Ibid.

26. T Bodenheimer, 'The HMO backlash – righteous or reactionary?' *New England Journal of Medicine*, 1996, 335, pp 1601-1604.

27. Ibid.

28. J P Bunker, 'Can professionalism survive in the marketplace?' *British Medical Journal*, 1994, 308, pp 1179-1180.

Chapter 7

1. Isobel Allen, *Doctors and their Careers*, London: PSI, 1994; see also, 'Doctors Under Stress', BMA News Review, April 1996, pp 32-34.

2. R S Downie, 'Professions and Professionalism', *Journal of Philosophy of Education*, 1990, 24, pp 147-159.

3. Ibid.

4. J Ellis, *The Story of the London Hospital Medical College*, 1986.

5. Robert G Brame, 'Professionalism, Physician Autonomy and the New

    Economics of Medicine', *American Journal of Obstetrics and Gynaecology*, 1994, 171, pp 293-297.

6. Emil Friedman, 'The Power of Physicians: Autonomy and Balance in a Changing System', *American Journal of Medicine*, 1995, 99, pp 579-587.

7. Donald W Light, 'Betrayal by the Surgeons', *Lancet*, 1996, 347, pp 812-813; see also, John Yates, *Private Eye, Heart and Hip: Surgical Consultants, the National Health Service and Private Medicine*, Churchill Livingstone, 1995.

8. Brame, op cit.

9. Roy Griffiths, *NHS Management Enquiry*, DHSS, 1983.

10. Norman Browse, 'Clincians Must Lead', *British Medical Journal*, 1996, 313, p 1268.

11. J Stewart Horner, 'The Management Myth', *Journal of the Royal College of Physicians*, 1997, 31, pp 149-152.

SOME PUBLICATIONS
FROM THE SOCIAL AFFAIRS UNIT

...on virtue and personal responsibility

FAKING IT

THE SENTIMENTALISATION OF MODERN SOCIETY

EDITED BY DIGBY ANDERSON & PETER MULLEN

Say 'fake' and one thinks of street sellers touting imitation brand perfumes and watches – or even fraud insurance or investments. But what if a society's central institutions were fakes – a school system with no education in it, a welfare system which actually promoted dependency not welfare, churches with no real religion in them?

Faking It charts the march of the fraudulent through modern society's institutions, through its government policies now obsessed with spin, image and gesture rather than substance, its sentimental environmental obsessions, its narcissistic, Godless religion, its elevation of fake feeling in novels and music.

Its authors, 12 distinguished academics, offer a frightening vision of a self-indulgent civilisation which cannot tell image from reality. It was this sentimental weakness for the fake which, above all else, explains the Diana funeral phenomenon in which sentimentality – mob grief – was personified and canonised and feeling exalted above reason, reality and restraint.

The woes of society – crime, broken families, falling school standards, confusion about morality and manners, are often attributed to bad ideas or perverted interests. It is not in fact ideas or interests which explain our decadence but feelings, sentimental feelings.

ISBN 0907631 75 4

£15.95

THE LOSS OF VIRTUE
moral confusion and social disorder in Britain and America

edited by Digby Anderson

A NATIONAL REVIEW BOOK

'...cogent, brave and timely...'
Catholic Herald

ISBN 0 907631 50 9   £15.95

THIS WILL HURT
the restoration of virtue and civic order

edited by Digby Anderson

A NATIONAL REVIEW BOOK

'The book reflects a strong trend in public debate, a move away from the economic preoccupations of the 1980s to concern for the social fabric... It is a merit of *This Will Hurt* that the authors confront the difficulties involved'
Sunday Telegraph

ISBN 0 907631 63 0   £15.95

GENTILITY RECALLED
'mere' manners and the making of social order

edited by Digby Anderson

Published in co-operation with the
Acton Institute for the Study of Religion and Liberty

'address[es] some real problems'
The Guardian

ISBN 0 907631 66 5   £15.95

LOYALTY MISPLACED
misdirected virtue and social disintegration

edited by Gerald frost

A discussion of the fissiparous tendencies in modern society, suggesting a range of contributory factors

ISBN 0 907631 70 3   £15.95

On health and lifestyle...

A Code of Ethics for Health Promotion
Michael Kelly
'This very important issue'
The Daily Telegraph
RESEARCH REPORT 23
ISBN 0 907631 68 1   £5.00

The Death of Humane Medicine and the Rise of Coercive Healthism
Petr Skrabanek
'This excellent book'   *The Independent*
ISBN 0 907631 59 2   £12.95

Take a Little Wine –or Beer or Whisky – for Your Stomach's Sake
Digby Anderson
ISBN 0 907631 60 6   £5.00

A New Diet of Reason:
healthy eating and government policy 1985-1995
David Conning
ISBN 0 907631 64 9   £5.00

Preventionitis: the exaggerated claims of health promotion
edited by James Le Fanu
ISBN 0 907631 58 4   £9.95

Health, Lifestyle and Environment: Countering the Panic
Published in co-operation with the Manhattan Institute
'suggests that the nation is gripped by a "health panic" generated by often contradictory advice from researchers'
The Times
ISBN 0 907631 44 4   £9.95

A Diet of Reason:
sense and nonsense in the healthy eating debate
edited by Digby Anderson
Casebound:ISBN 0 907631 26 6 £9.95
Paperback:ISBN 0 907631 22 3 £5.95

Drinking to Your Health:
The allegations and the evidence
edited by Digby Anderson
ISBN 0 907631 37 1   £14.95

On education and training...

A Ballon Waiting to be Burst?
Pseudomanagement training
Stephen Williams
ISBN 0 907631 67 3 £5.00

Educational Achievement in Japan:
lessons for the west
Richard Lynn
Published in co-operation with the
Macmillan Press
'...finds that teacher motivation in
Japan is fuelled by two factors: having
to teach to a national curriculum and
working in schools which have to
compete on results to survive'
Times Educational Supplement
ISBN 0 333 44532 5 £8.95

The Wayward Curriculum:
a cause for parents' concern?
edited by Dennis O'Keeffe
ISBN 0 907631 19 3 £9.95

Schooling for British Muslims:
integrated, opted out or
denominational?
Mervyn Hiskett
RESEARCH REPORT 12
ISBN 0 907631 33 9 £4.50

Trespassing? Businessmen's views
on the education system
Michael Brophy et al
ISBN 0 907631 11 8 £2.95

Educated for employment?
Digby Anderson et al
ISBN 0 907631 03 7 £2.65

The Pied Pipers of Education
Antony Flew et al
ISBN 0 907631 02 9 £2.65

Detecting Bad Schools:
a guide for normal parents
Digby Anderson
ISBN 0 907631 04 5 £1.00

On economic and corporate affairs...

Corporate Irresponsibility: is business appeasing anti-business activists?
RESEARCH REPORT 26
Robert Halfon
ISBN 0 907631 78 9 £5.00

No Man Can Serve Two Masters: shareholders versus stakeholders in the governance of companies
RESEARCH REPORT 25
Joseph F Johnston
ISBN 0 907631 76 2 £6.00

The Corporation Under Siege: exposing the devices used by activists and regulators in the non-risk society
Mark Neal & Christie Davies
ISBN 0 907631 77 0 £9.95

The Secret of the Miracle Economy: different national attitudes to competitiveness and money
Richard Lynn
'reports only "competitiveness" is significantly connected with economic growth'
Financial Times
ISBN 0 907631 41 X £8.95

Set Fair: a gradualist proposal for privatising weather forecasting
Jerome Ellig
RESEARCH REPORT 13
ISBN 0 907631 34 7 £4.50

On consumer affairs...

What has 'Ethical Investment' to do with Ethics?
Digby Anderson et al
RESEARCH REPORT 21
ISBN 0 907631 65 7 £5.00

Keeping Cures from Patients: the perverse effects of pharmaceutical regulations
Mark Neal
ISBN 0 907631 62 2 £5.00

False Economies: the true cost of 'cheap' drugs
Diane B Fairweather & Ian Hindmarch
ISBN 0 907631 61 4 £5.00

Reaching for the counter. The new child consumers: regulation or education?
Adrian Furnham
ISBN 0 907631 54 1 £7.50

Risk, Health and the Consumer
James McCormick & Digby Anderson
ISBN 0 907631 47 9 £3.50

Consumer Debt: whose responsibility?
K Alec Chrystal
ISBN 0 907631 39 8 £3.50

Advertising Bans: administrative decisions or matters of principle?
John Gray
ISBN 0 907631 43 6 £4.00
Also available in Spanish translation

Advertising Bans: consequences for consumers
Mark Bentley & Mai Fyfield
ISBN 0 907631 45 2 £4.00

Biotechnology Regulation: the unacceptable costs of excessive caution
Henry I Miller
RISK CONTROVERSIES 8
ISBN 0 907631 69 X £5.00

On the welfare state...

**A Phantom Carnage:
the myth that low income kills**
James Le Fanu
RESEARCH REPORT 17
ISBN 0 907631 51 7   £5.00

**Magic in the Surgery. Counselling
in the NHS: a licensed state
friendship service**
Myles Harris
RESEARCH REPORT 20
ISBN 0 907631 56 8   £5.00

**Popular Attitudes to State Welfare
Services: a growing demand for
alternatives?**
Peter Saunders & Colin Harris
'suggest[s] that the public feels
"trapped" into supporting state
services by taxation because people are
unwilling or unable to pay twice'
                                     Sunday Times
RESEARCH REPORT 11
ISBN 0 907631 30 4   £3.00

**Breaking the Spell of the Welfare
State**
*Digby Anderson, June Lait & David
Marsland*
ISBN 0 907631 00 2   £2.65

**The Megaphone Solution:
government attempts to cure social
problems with mass media
campaigns**
Digby Anderson
RESEARCH REPORT 9
ISBN 0 907631 28 2   £3.00

On family matters...

**Families in Dreamland: challenging
the new consensus for state
childcare**
Patricia Morgan
RESEARCH REPORT 15
ISBN 0 907631 48 7   £4.00

**The Unmentionable Face of
Poverty: domestic incompetence,
improvidence and male
irresponsibility in low income
families**
Digby Anderson
ISBN 0 907631 42 8   £4.00

Finding Fault in Divorce
George Brown
MORAL ASPECTS OF SOCIAL PROBLEMS 2
ISBN 0 907631 35 5   £3.50

**Full Circle: bringing up children in
the post-permissive society**
edited by Digby Anderson
ISBN 0 9076331 29 0   £8.95

**Denying Homes to Black Children:
Britain's new race adoption policies**
David Dale
RESEARCH REPORT 8
ISBN 0 907631 32 1   £3.50

On moral and social issues...

Why Social Policy Cannot be Morally Neutral: the current confusion about pluralism
Basil Mitchell
ISBN 0 907631 35 5   £3.50

Self-Improvement and Social Action
Antony Flew
ISBN 0 907631 36 3   £3.50

The Kindness that Kills: the churches' simplistic response to complex social issues
edited by Digby Anderson
Commissioned by the SAU
and published by SPCK
ISBN 0 281 04096 6   £3.95

Wealth and Poverty: a Jewish analysis
Jonathan Sacks
ISBN 0 907631 15 0   £2.00

The Bible, Justice and the Culture of Poverty: emotive calls to action versus rational analysis
Irving Hexham
ISBN 0 907631 16 9   £2.00

The Philosophy of Poverty: Good Samaritans or Procrusteans?
Antony Flew
ISBN 0 907631 17 7   £2.00

The Christian Response to Poverty: working with God's economic laws
James Sadowsky
ISBN 0 907621 18 5   £2.00

Do Animals Have Rights?
Tibor Machan
ISBN 0 907631 40 1   £3.50

On the environment and housing...

NonSense About Nature
Anthony O'Hear
RISK CONTROVERSIES 9
ISBN 0 907631 72 X   £5.00

Environmental Alarums: a medical audit of environmental damage to human health
James Le Fanu
RISK CONTROVERSIES 3
ISBN 0 907631 57 6   £5.00

After Government Failure?
D R Denman
ISBN 0 907631 24 X   £2.50

Planning Fails the Inner Cities
R N Goodchild & D R Denman
ISBN 0 907631 25 8   £2.50

Caring for the Countryside: public dependence on private interest
Barry Bracewell-Milnes
ISBN 0 907631 27 4   £2.50

Home Truths: essays on housing
Barbara Robson et al
ISBN 0 907631 05 3   £2.95

Asian Housing in Britain
Jon Davies
RESEARCH REPORT 6
ISBN 0 907631 13 4   £2.00

On the United Nations...

Chattering International: how Unicef fails the world's poorest children
James Le Fanu
RESEARCH REPORT 19
ISBN 0 907631 53 3 £5.00

Who Benefits from WHO? The decline of the World Health Organization
Robert D Tollison & Richard E Wagner
RESEARCH REPORT 18
ISBN 0 907631 55 X £5.00

Who Needs WHO? Three views on the World Health Organization's dietary guidelines
Petr Skrabanek, Mike Gibney & James Le Fanu
RESEARCH REPORT 16
ISBN 0 907631 49 £5.00

And...

The British Woman Today: A qualitative survey of the images in women's magazines
Edited by Digby Anderson & Michael Mosbacher
ISBN 0 907631 74 6 £7.50

The Silencing of Society: the true cost of the lust for news
Kenneth Minogue
ISBN 0 907631 71 8 £7.50

Unwelcome Truths: Edmund Burke on today's political conceits
Ian Crowe
RESEARCH REPORT 24
ISBN 0 907631 71 1 £5.00

Extra Dry: columns in The Times
Digby Anderson
'imperative writing on political and social subjects'
The Spectator
ISBN 0 907631 12 6 £2.95

The Social Affairs Unit

The SAU is an independent research and educational trust committed to the promotion of lively and wide-ranging debate on social affairs. Its authors — over 200 — have analyzed the factors which make for a free and orderly society in which enterprise can flourish. It is committed to international co-operation in ideas: eg *The Loss of Virtue* and *This Will Hurt* published as **National Review Books**, *Gentility Recalled* published in co-operation with the Acton Institute and joint Anglo-European projects on food and alcohol policy. Current areas of work include consumer affairs, the critical appraisal of welfare and public spending and problems of freedom and personal responsibility.

The Unit's impact and funding

The Times writes:
The Social Affairs Unit is famous for driving its coach and horses through the liberal consensus, scattering intellectual picket lines as it goes. It is equally famous for raising questions which strike most people most of the time as too dangerous or too difficult to think about.

To maintain its independence, the Unit is funded by a wide range of foundations and trusts, sales of its publications and corporate donations from highly diverse sectors. It has received support from over 100 sources. The SAU is registered as an educational charity, number 281530.

The Social Affairs Unit
Suite 5/6 1st Floor
Morley House
Regent Street
London W1R 5AB